ISLAND OF ADVENTURE

Ross E. Hutchins

ISLAND OF ADVENTURE

A Naturalist Explores a Gulf Coast Wilderness

ILLUSTRATED WITH PHOTOGRAPHS
BY THE AUTHOR

C 3

DODD, MEAD & COMPANY · NEW YORK

TO "CAPTAIN" H. L. VICKERS,
skipper of the *Likilikit,* in memory of
pleasant days and nights on the
Singing River

Introduction

THIS, IN A SENSE, is a romance, the story of one man's love for an island, an island that has no name. It is but one of many such islands—larger than most—found in the wet hinterland along the Gulf of Mexico. To the osprey, wheeling aloft in the summer sky, the island is not obvious because there is no sharp line of demarcation between it and the marsh grass sea around it.

One branch of the wide Pascagoula River flows slowly past The Island but, here, it can only be called a river by courtesy since its flow is governed by the nearby Gulf and its tides.

The Island's forest is deep and gloomy, inhabited by a wide variety of creatures that dwell in the trees, upon the ground, and in a hidden cypress lake. This forest is semitropical in luxuriance; the trees are draped with lianas armed with vicious thorns, and, in many places, growths of bamboo-like cane make travel most difficult. The sun, filtering down through the leafy forest canopy, takes on a greenish quality and bathes the earth below in a dim, eerie light in which orchids and spider lilies thrive and where colorful fungi push up through the black humus.

To the casual visitor, this island may seem brooding and mysterious, with danger lurking in every shadow. But the only real dangers lie in the cottonmouth moccasins that sun themselves along the shores of the island and the bayous and in the rattlesnakes that hide among the palmettos. In truth, a person is actually far safer here than on a busy city street.

Both The Island and the surrounding marshland are endowed with a species of timeless beauty that is felt as well as seen, and the visitor is always entranced by broad vistas of waving grass stretching away, at some points, to far horizons, by stately, moss-draped cypresses along the meandering bayous, and by the dark, jungle-like forest that clothes the areas of higher ground. The Island rises above the river but actually belongs to it because the river, long ago, created it from silt carried down from inland hills.

This, then, is the setting for our story. It is a place known to many men—the fishermen and hunters who come in motorboats that cleave the waters, causing the fringing grasses and reeds to rasp one against the other with soft, sibilant sounds. But when the boats are gone and the discordant echoes of their motors have faded away, the waters become quiet again, quickly erasing all record of human visitation. This marshy wilderness has been the same for a million years and men do not change it; they come but they do not remain, and their visits are but small incidents in this realm of water and earth and sky. Like all wild places, the marshland is completely impersonal; it cares not whether I or its native inhabitants live or die. Only the ever-present buzzards circling slowly in the sky above it are concerned, and their interests are selfish.

Such is my island; a naturalist's paradise where, during happy days and nights, I have explored its hidden places and thrilled at the sights and sounds of its teeming life in a setting as wild and uninhibited as can still be found on the mainland of North America.

                                                              R.E.H.

Contents

ISLAND OF ADVENTURE

Chapter 1

ISLAND SANCTUARY

THE DICTIONARY DEFINES an island as a piece of land surrounded by water, but smaller than a continent. This, of course, is a barren statement, telling nothing of the true nature of islands, whether they be arctic islands amid shifting ice floes or tropical islands surrounded by palms and bathed in warm trade winds. Islands, like people, have varied personalities. The origin of the word itself is lost in the dim mists of time. Such bits of isolated land were once called *ylands* but the Anglo-Saxon word was *egland* which apparently had its origin in *ea* or *eg* meaning "water or river" and *lond* meaning "land." Thus, the original meaning, seemingly, indicated an area of land in the water.

Islands are usually thought of as places apart from the greater land expanses where men live by the sweat of their brows; islands are retreats from the workaday world of industry and commerce. Men often retreat, or have the desire to retreat, to some island when the problems of their world become too great and the pressures of civilization too weighty. Here, in fancy, at least, they feel cut off from care and the real world seems far away. But islands have an appeal that goes far beyond all such practical considerations; perhaps we unconsciously associate islands with our inner selves. Each of us, in a sense, lives in a secluded, personal island that is either happy or filled with hidden fears, depending on circumstances. Each of us is a separate entity, isolated from other men by a gulf

1

that cannot be bridged, even by those who are closest to us. This, perhaps, is the real secret of the strange lure of islands; psychologically, they are merely extensions of our inner selves. Significantly, the word isolate is derived from *isola*, a word meaning island.

Each one of us is an island, yet we are tied to each other by invisible bonds and men cannot for long exist alone. The severest punishment meted out to a criminal is solitary confinement, and even a rat, ostracized by its fellows, soon dies, though surrounded by abundant food. More than three hundred years ago, John Donne wrote:

> "No man is an Island, entire of itselfe; everyman is a piece of the continent, a part of the maine; if a clod bee washed away by the sea, Europe is the lesse, as well as if the Promontorie were, as well as if a Mannor of thy friends or thine owne were; any man's death diminishes me, because I am involved in Mankinde; And therefore never send to know for whom the bell tolls; it tolls for thee."

Like many people, I have often dreamed of owning an island retreat, some tropical Shangri-La set down in a cobalt-blue sea. In my mind's eye it is complete with palms swaying gracefully in the trade wind and surrounded by a fringing coral reef where white-capped breakers curl over and spill endlessly on the beach. In imagination, I even hear the thundering sounds of the water pounding upon snow-white sand. Once I had the good fortune to live for a time on such an island, but I have never actually owned one. Islands are hard to come by and only the privileged few can actually own or live on one. How often we read in the daily press that some man has purchased a small boat or ship in which he and his family hope to sail to the South Seas to "get away from it all." No doubt such men labor under the misapprehension that there are thousands of uninhabited islands where a family can settle down amid tropical verdure and exist on a diet of coconuts and bananas. Unfortunately, such a life under exotic conditions has its drawbacks, as these families soon discover. In most instances, they return a year or so later, saddened and disillusioned by a dream that did

Cypress-lined bayou leading to the island the author claims as his own. The swaying streamers of moss impart an exotic atmosphere.

not come true. Few people who have lived their lives amid the conveniences of civilization are capable of suddenly transplanting themselves into primitive surroundings, however idyllic they may seem. Still, islands have a fascination that transcends all logic and most of us thrill to such tales as that of Robinson Crusoe and the true story of the mutineers of H.M.S. *Bounty* on lonely Pitcairn Island.

Even some wild creatures—the albatross, for instance—are attracted to certain islands as if drawn by some far-reaching magnetic force. The Laysan albatross, with a wingspread as great as the eagle's, wanders for months at a time over the vast stretches of the Pacific Ocean from the coast of China to the shores of America, "lone wandering but not lost." These birds roam over the limitless face of the world's greatest ocean and then, during November and December, locate without error a certain tiny island set down in the lonely expanse of water where for countless generations they have reared their young. Why one special island? There are thousands of islands scattered like gems across the watery reaches of the vast Pacific, but only one island will do. Men navigate across this ocean, guided by sextant, chronometer, and compass, yet the albatross returns unerringly year after year to the same island to nest, a feat no human could accomplish without the aid of complex instruments.

Why man's interest in islands? Truly, it is difficult to explain in any very logical manner. In medieval days, islands were often chosen as sites for fortified castles because they were easily defended, but this was before the days of modern weapons such as airplanes and atomic bombs. Still, even today, islands are difficult to invade, as witness the bitter struggles on the beaches of Iwo Jima, Guam, and Tarawa. To a biologist there are islands of many types. On the prairies of our Midwest there are oak "islands," large groves of oak trees so isolated from other forests that they harbor a special fauna and flora. Here live fox squirrels and woodland birds not found anywhere else in the vicinity. Scattered here and there on these same prairies are pothole lakes, mere pools of water, so remote from other bodies of water that their aquatic inhabitants are almost as isolated from other, similar forms of life, as if sur-

In the Everglades, the small, tree-covered patches of high ground are known as hammocks. The word is of Seminole origin meaning "a garden place." Such hammocks are separated from others by vast stretches of grassy marsh.

rounded by walls. Here, dragonflies live for many generations with little or no contact with individuals of other lakes. A mountaintop may also be an island since, climatically, its plant and animal life is segregated from that of other mountaintops. The high, wind-swept ridges of our western mountains are the habitat of large, attractive, white butterflies with crimson spots on their wings. Known to zoologists as *Parnassius* butterflies, their caterpillars feed upon low-growing stonecrop and saxifrage and I have never encountered the adults anywhere except on the Rockies. Similar butterflies occur also in the Alps and on mountains in Asia. Those living on one mountaintop have little or no contact with those on other mountains. For all practical purposes, their mountaintop habitats are biological islands.

Many oceanic islands have been isolated for such long periods that the fauna and flora of each one is characteristic. When early explorers arrived in the Hawaiian Islands they encountered many unfamiliar birds, including the Laysan teal and the Laysan rail, the latter bird with a voice like a tinkling bell.

The plant life of islands is not as restricted as is the animal life. The seeds of plants may easily be transported from island to island by winds and ocean currents, resulting in continual mingling and additions. I have often found sea beans washed up along island beaches and almost every tropical island has its shorelines ringed by stranded coconuts. The spores of lichens, ferns, and algae may

easily float in air. Thus these simple forms of plant life are usually the first to appear on newly formed islands.

As far as the evolution of island animal life is concerned, the Galápagos Islands are the most interesting of all. These islands lie six hundred miles west of South America and are of rather recent origin; it is estimated that they arose from the sea by volcanic activity about a million years ago. The plants and animals found there somehow arrived from the mainland of South America. There are birds of many kinds as well as giant tortoises and yard-long iguanas. But most remarkable of all the inhabitants of these remote islands are the finches. Apparently, only one species originally became established on the islands but, through isolation and the slow processes of natural selection, thirteen different species, each with its own characteristics and habits, have evolved. Indeed, it was these finches that first planted in the mind of Charles Darwin his concept of the origin of species by evolution as contrasted to special creation.

Islands arise in various ways; sometimes they are merely extensions of land that have been cut off by erosion or tidal action; in other cases, they arise from the sea by volcanic activity. In time,

Some islands are born in violence accompanied by the ejection of hot lava from deep within the ocean. When this lava has cooled, plant life arrives in the form of seeds and spores and the island is eventually clothed with vegetation. This is an island being formed by volcanic eruption in the western Pacific.

This log floating down a tropical river is covered with plants, and may also be carrying insects, spiders, and other animals. If it should eventually drift away to a distant island and be washed ashore, its plant and animal life might become established there.

plants of various kinds become established, having arrived by air or by sea. But animal life is slower to appear; the chances are small of land-inhabiting animals successfully crossing long stretches of open sea. The Hawaiian Islands, for example, originally had no mammals except bats, which were of North American types. Of animal life, insects and spiders are apt to be the first to be found on new islands, arriving perhaps as stowaways on drifting logs. I have often seen such logs floating down toward the sea in tropical rivers, each one covered with a dense growth of plants. Hidden among this vegetation, I am sure, were insects, spiders, and perhaps other small creatures. Now you may say that the chances are remote of such a log drifting across the sea and being washed up on a beach with its passengers still alive. In this you would be correct. Yet, if one such log were to be carried to an island every thousand years, that island would eventually acquire a fauna and flora of its own. An island has plenty of time.

If you have ever cruised through tropical seas you have noticed that the first hint of an island landfall is a snow-white line of breakers thundering over the reef. Out beyond the shores of these islands there is usually a fringing reef and, between it and the island, a quiet lagoon. The open sea is deep cobalt-blue, but the

Above: *Here, exposed at low tide, a tropical coral reef stretches away to white surf thundering over its outer edge. Beyond, a volcanic promontory thrusts toward the open sea.* Left: *Close-up of coral, the building material of tropical islands. Composed of hard calcium, these skeletons of coral animals accumulate in thick beds, on top of which sand and soil are deposited.*

water of the lagoon is pea-green in color. This is because the water of the lagoon is shallow and filled with microscopic plant and animal life whereas the open sea contains little life and is blue because it is deep.

The circular reefs which enclose most of these tropical islands have been created by living coral animals. Corals are low forms of animal life—soft, fleshy, and of small size, yet capable of extracting calcium carbonate or lime from sea water and depositing it around themselves to form protective skeletons. In time, these tiny coral animals die but the hard skeletons they secreted remain. New corals build their intricate abodes upon those of their ancestors and so on *ad infinitum*. In this manner, a coral reef grows ever larger, rising up to slightly above the level of the water's surface. If the island slowly sinks, the corals multiply upward. Since they are alive and continually growing, the reefs they form are not mere deposits of lime slowly being worn down by wave action. A coral reef is thus a living thing consisting of coral polyp animals growing upon the stony remains of their forebears.

Probably the most attractive islands of the tropical Pacific are the atolls, circular strings of islets, often many miles across. Always these circular island chains surround a central lagoon into which there are often breaks or passages where ships may enter and find safe anchorage. Atolls and their plant and animal life are fascinating, but most remarkable of all is the manner in which atolls were formed. Probably it was like this. Long ago a volcanic eruption from the floor of the Pacific pushed molten lava upward toward the surface amid violent explosions and escaping gases. The surrounding sea was turned into a boiling caldron and hot steam floated away across the water. Eventually the volcanic activity subsided and the lava cooled; the years passed. Plants arrived in the form of floating seeds and soon the island was covered by green vegetation. Surrounding the island there developed the usual fringing coral reef. Time passed and slowly the island's stony surface was eroded away or subsided and, eventually, it no longer rose above the level of the surrounding sea; the place where the island had been became a shallow lagoon. But, since the surrounding reef was composed of living coral, it continued to grow and thus did not disappear. Portions of the reef accumulated sand and, here and there, various plants and trees took root, forming small islets. Where there had once been a large island surrounded by a coral reef, there was eventually a central lagoon ringed by small islets, each set with graceful palms. This is an atoll and thus was it formed.

The wide Pascagoula River, seen from one of the many narrow bayous. During a portion of each day the river reverses itself and flows northward as a result of the tide.

The islands along the northern portion of the Gulf of Mexico, by contrast, had uneventful births; they came into being very slowly and their inception was not accompanied by earthquakes or volcanic fire. Enclosed within and among the branching mouths of the Pascagoula River just before it flows into the Gulf are numerous bits of higher land that are, in truth, islands. One of these, perhaps a hundred acres in extent, I claim as mine. The dark soil which supports its jungle-like forest was carried down from the higher ground to the north and deposited, a bit at a time, by the meandering river whose waters, slowed down by their approach to the Gulf of Mexico, could no longer hold its silt in suspension. Originally, the place where the island now lies was covered by the sea, but the river, toiling ceaselessly, slowly transported the land-forming silt and filled in the shallow estuary, pushing the coastline outward a little more each year. This same river, seemingly never satisfied with its work, continued to mold and reform the land that it had created, aided by the earth's internal forces which, here and there, slowly pushed the land upward or allowed it to subside. During times of flood the river cut away some pieces of land and dropped the debris in other places. Ever restless, the river periodically changed its channels and created new passages. And so my island came into being, the end result of restless water being lifted up by the sun and falling upon the land, striving always to return to its ancient abode, the sea.

I do not know who actually owns my island, and I care not whose name is on record in official land titles. Perhaps this piece of high ground belongs to no one; certainly, I know of no human owner. As far as I am concerned, it belongs to me and to the creatures that dwell there and, for lack of a better name, I call it The Island.

Like the birds that "stake out" their nesting territories, a naturalist may often "own" a piece of land without due process of law. After all, legal possession of real estate is a passing thing. The formal terminology on the deed, all properly recorded, may read, "To be held by him, his heirs, and assignees forever." But this is mere optimism, because nations and civilizations come and go, land boundaries are forgotten and their records lost. Long before the present legal owner of The Island, if there is one, came into possession, it belonged to the Indians who perhaps camped upon its

Afternoon sun bathes the gray-green drapery of Spanish moss with light. The wet savannah beyond the bayou channel is the habitat of many birds, mammals, and reptiles.

high ground. After the Indians came the Spanish, then the French, and finally the English. But this did not change The Island because its forest jungle had little commercial value and could not be used for economic gain.

And so, down the years, The Island has changed hardly at all. It probably looks today almost as it did the day Columbus discovered America. Its trees grow old and crash to the earth during autumn gales; year by year, falling leaves add more humus to its forest floor, while twining roots creep down its banks, capturing additional soil from the passing water, slowly enlarging The Island's area. The seasons come and go and time moves slowly. Great snapping turtles sun themselves indolently upon the surrounding sandbars and white egrets wade slowly through the shallow waters. Bitterns stalk minnows in the estuaries, fading mysteriously from sight when danger threatens. Overhead, buzzards circle slowly, their keen eyes searching the ground for gruesome booty. Here, too, is the home of the alligator. The Island is a small world of life, a microcosm set apart from the greater land. During the day and during the night, within its boundaries, are played the quiet dramas of wild places, dramas that are often tragedies. Such is my island.

The Island is located along the western shore of the West Branch of the Pascagoula River and is an area of higher ground surrounded by open savannah dotted here and there with other small forested "islands," few of which have names. Only the bayous and lakes are designated on maps because only they are accessible by boat. The meandering water courses bear intriguing names—Buzzard Bayou, Swift Bayou, Crooked Bayou, Snake Bayou, Moon Lake, and Dead River, all descriptive, in some manner, of real or fancied characteristics.

The Island lies among the endlessly twisting channels of the great Pascagoula River system shortly before they empty into the Gulf of Mexico. This stream, known to the Indians as The Singing River, divides into numerous passages as it meanders southward through the marshy savannah and you can best appreciate its extent when I tell you that there are more than a thousand miles of chan-

The island's edge imparts an aspect of tropical luxuriance. Orchids, ferns, and other small plants push up through the black soil, while palmettos, bay, and other trees and shrubs grow in profusion. Beyond the shore, the forest is deep and dark.

nels and bayous, all interconnected in a confusing network. My island is remote, lonely, and isolated, and in this, to me, lies its fascination. It is my refuge where I have returned again and again to revel in its solitude and to probe into its mysteries. Every man, in fact or fancy, has an island. This island is mine.

Chapter 2

TO THE ISLAND

MY FIRST TRIP to The Island began on a warm day in late autumn when the bald cypresses along the bayous were tinged with rust-colored foliage. Unlike most other conifers, these cypresses are deciduous and would, I knew, eventually shed their foliage, leaving gaunt limbs etched against the winter sky. My conveyence was a houseboat or, more properly, a river yacht, named the *Likilikit*. My companions and I had gone aboard the boat at an isolated fishing camp hidden deeply in the vast Pascagoula Swamp. We had taken on stores of gasoline and food sufficient to last a week, since, once we left the dock, there would be no further contact with civilization until our return.

The *Likilikit* is thirty-five feet long and of shallow draft, ideally suited to bayou and river cruising. Like a seagoing vessel, it is self-contained, having all the conveniences and luxuries needed for a pleasant life beyond the borders of civilization. My companions were fishermen and, like all devotees of that sport, had only one thing in mind—the catching of fish. As is usual on most such expeditions of which I am a part, I was the offbeat character, tolerated but not exactly understood because my interests are unusual. While others are fishing or engaging in "normal" pursuits, I am turning over logs to see what is hidden underneath, or collecting and photographing plant and animal specimens. It is all a matter of personal interest. I have no patience with fishing, not being content to spend hours on end waiting for some fish to bite my hook. What is even

LIKILIKIT

The houseboat Likilikit *is self-contained, ideally suited to cruising along bayous and rivers. It contains every facility for comfort beyond the borders of civilization.*

more inexplicable to most people is the fact that almost any fish I do get my hands on goes into a jar of alcohol or formaldehyde to be preserved for future study. But I have become accustomed to being considered a little peculiar and am happy that some people do try to understand my interests and even attempt to help me.

My usual gear for such an expedition consists of about a hundred pounds of photographic equipment, plus jars of preservative and collecting nets. On this trip I was advised to purchase a fishing license, since it was unlikely that a local game warden could ever be convinced that I had merely "come along for the ride." This would be just too unbelievable since, as far as most people are concerned, no one ever goes into the Pascagoula Swamp except to fish. So, in order to forestall possible embarrassment, I acquired a license allowing me to catch fish even though I had not the slightest intention of "wetting a hook."

Shortly after noon, the houseboat's motors were stimulated into throbbing life by their starters and the boat was no longer a dead thing floating on the brown water of the bayou. It strained at the ropes holding it to the dock, and when these were cast off we moved slowly down the narrow channel, the propellers churning

The author sits in the bow of the houseboat as it follows the winding bayou.

Cruising down the bayou, the houseboat follows a tortuous channel between grassy banks that are often bordered by moss-draped cypresses.

up the mud and disturbing the green fronds of the water plants growing on the bottom.

I climbed to the top deck of the houseboat. There, fifteen feet above the water, I watched in fascination while we followed the tortuous channel that meandered away across the marsh grass plain. Here and there, colorful blooms added gay touches to the otherwise pastel landscape stretching away to the horizon. The channel of the bayou was often barely wide enough to permit the boat to pass, and from my vantage point I could see, far away, other channels that wound away across the grassy plain, their courses marked, here and there, by rows of cypresses both living and dead. Lonely crows often sat quietly upon dead snags while birds of many other kinds fluttered over the waving grass. Once, as we rounded a bend, a small alligator lay half-asleep in the water, but, as we approached, it slowly sank from sight and was seen no more.

The cypresses along the bayou were all draped with long streamers of gray Spanish moss swaying gently in the breeze. It was like a scene out of some childhood fantasy, strange, exotic, unreal, languid. I felt as if I were living in some fanciful dream world as the changing scene slowly unfolded, bend after bend. Now and again the channel widened and mudbanks appeared where snowy egrets waded sedately in the shallows, their white forms reflected in the still waters. Sometimes muskrats sat half-hidden among the stems of the tall marsh grasses beyond the water's edge. Elevated as I was, above the waving grass, I had a bird's-eye view of my surroundings. Now and again, some distance beyond the channel, I could see moving grass where some creature crept through the vegetation, but I never had a glimpse of the animals and to this day have no idea what was there. Occasionally, above the muffled sound of the boat's motors, I could hear distant bird calls, but the birds that uttered them were hidden from view.

It was all intriguing and mysterious and I longed to explore this grassy world at closer range. The tide was out, with the result that the water was draining from the marsh, leaving the soft black muck exposed. Out of this muck grew the dense stand of marsh grasses and other vegetation, the bases of their stems discolored and crowded close together. Here and there between these stems ran dark passages which appeared to be inhabited by some sort of animals, but we passed along too rapidly for me to determine what they were; this was a matter that would have to wait. Always, a naturalist is faced with the same problem; he travels across the sea or along a highway at high speed and sees places or things he would like to explore in detail but time does not permit it. This is very frustrating. A quick look is useless; to learn what is going on, one must quietly explore and study details. The difference between mere "looking" and really "seeing" becomes important. It is one thing to catch a glimpse of a fallen tree from a highway and quite another thing to examine in detail the mossy growth covering its bark. Once while cruising in tropical seas I saw numerous flying fish sailing away from the ship, but I was not satisfied until I had captured a specimen and held it in my hand in order to study it in detail. Thus, a naturalist needs his own personal transportation; he cannot make worthwhile observations while traveling at high speed across land or sea. In addition, he must usually work alone. A naturalist's life may be somewhat lonely, but it has compensations.

As the houseboat cruised down the twisting bayou I continued my vigil from the upper deck, sweeping the marshy world beyond the channel with a powerful telescope to obtain a closer look at the passing scene. At last the bayou widened and then emptied into a broad expanse of water that was actually the main channel of the sluggish Pascagoula River. The waters were coffee-brown and flowed gently along between high banks beyond which rose large trees, all festooned with a drapery of gray-green moss.

The houseboat swung out into the current of the river and headed north, following closely along the western bank. Water birds, alarmed by our passing, took wing and flew up the river; otherwise, there were no other evidences of life except turtles sunning themselves on infrequent sandbars and half-submerged logs. Sometimes the banks were heavily forested; at other times we passed growths of tall marsh grass which waved rhymically in the

Along the edges of the bayou, the roots of trees twine about each other in a tortured embrace. Forced to the surface by abundant moisture, these roots help to hold the soil against the eroding action of the tides.

undulations created by the boat. Once, as we rounded a bend, a number of large, yellow butterflies were seen crossing the river toward the east. They fluttered along, low over the water, and then away through the forest as if following a compass course. Now and again large dragonflies alighted upon the houseboat, their cellophane-like wings momentarily at rest. They perched quietly for a few seconds, then were off again, darting rapidly over the water.

Eventually, after several miles, we rounded an abrupt bend and came to a straight section of river where a meandering bayou opened into it, creating an island that was higher than the other surrounding land. The island was dominated by tall, spreading live oaks, some of which leaned far out over the river. Beneath the trees, along the sandy shore, rose a dense growth of palmettos, their fan-like fronds imparting a tropical atmosphere. Unknown to me, this was to become my island, a parcel of high ground surrounded by brown waters. In time I would come to know its intimate details like the palm of my hand. Eventually, I would learn many of its secrets and become familiar with the lives of its inhabitants. I had found my Shangri-La, though it would require time for this realization to dawn on me.

After snubbing the boat securely to a stout, overhanging cypress, my companions prepared to try their luck at fishing. I had other ideas. Rigging a gangplank, I stepped ashore, feeling much as Christopher Columbus must have felt when he landed at last on an island of the New World. But, of course, I was not the first visitor to The Island, as I very quickly discovered when I came upon the charred remains of a campfire not far inland. Still, there were no signs of recent occupation and so I soon began to consider that the island was mine by right of discovery.

On this first reconnaissance I found the island to be about a hundred acres in extent. Near its center was a cypress-ringed lake of considerable size. Along its muddy margins grew an almost impenetrable barrier of bamboo or cane and buttonbushes. The rest of the island was covered by dense, jungle-like vegetation, making exploration quite difficult.

After a general survey of the island I sat down on a rotting log and quietly took stock of my surroundings. Above me towered a great live oak, its trunk nearly a yard in diameter. Ten feet from the ground the first large branch emerged and extended out over a marshy area for nearly twenty feet. Gnarled and twisted by time and past hurricanes, its bark was deeply fissured and along its top grew masses of epiphytic ferns and mosses. Beyond the oak lay the

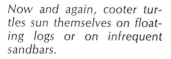

Now and again, cooter turtles sun themselves on floating logs or on infrequent sandbars.

open water of the lake and, as I watched, a bright-red male cardinal dropped down in a shaft of sunlight and alighted on a bush. He sat quietly for a time, then hopped down to the ground, looking in all directions. Soon I became aware of his more somber-colored mate, who was perched some distance away. After a minute or so she joined him and they continued to search their surroundings for any sign of danger—at least such was my interpretation of their actions. As I sat quietly observing them it gradually dawned on me

The houseboat is tied up beside The Island beneath the overhanging limbs of cypresses and red bay, all draped with Spanish moss.

Below: *Edge of the jungle. At some points along the bayou stretch areas of high ground clothed with dense growths of live oak heavily draped with moss.*

This large live oak is burdened with suspended Spanish moss that sways gently in the breeze. The moss is an epiphyte, belonging to the pineapple family.

that they had something in mind, that all this searching had some purpose. After a time, the male, satisfied at last that it was safe, flew down to a small pool and began fluttering his wings, tossing up a spray of droplets that sparkled in the sun. Now I knew why they had been so concerned about possible enemies. In bathing, a bird's feathers become wet and flight is difficult. This is the way of all wild creatures; eternal vigilance is a necessity to survival. One moment of laxity and some enemy is apt to exact its toll. Always, it is a game of life or death. Even such a simple act as bathing in a woodland pool must be accompanied by elaborate precautions.

After a few seconds of bathing, the male cardinal flew up to a low bush and fluttered his wings to shake out the water. Then, while he preened his feathers, the female flew down and took her turn.

This little woodland tableau which I had witnessed was nothing unusual; one can see cardinals bathing in any backyard birdbath. Yet, I was an unseen observer of the careful precautions taken by wild birds.

After the cardinals had finished their toilets and departed, I con-

tinued to sit on the log, enjoying the island's remoteness and solitude. Upon a nearby limb I detected a movement and then, as my
eyes became adjusted, I found that I was looking at a green chameleon. As I watched, it turned from green to brown and then to
green again. When it slowly lifted its head, its throat pouch pushed
downward, exposing an area of red skin. Several times it followed
this procedure, bobbing its head up and down. This, I knew, was a
male engaged in its mating ritual, but I saw no female and he soon
became interested in a fly which had alighted on a nearby leaf.
Rapidly his tongue flashed out and the luckless fly was gone. On
another tree I saw two blue-tailed skinks or lizards chasing each
other. Around and around the tree they ran, then disappeared into
a tree hole and I saw them no more.

For a long while I sat on the log watching the play of woodland
life going on around me in this undisturbed and isolated habitat.
Slowly the light faded from the sky and dusk descended over the
island and the marshland. From far away I heard the bellow of a
bull alligator and the evening cries of marsh birds. From willows

*The oval leaves of spatterdock (Nuphar) float upon the quiet waters of the
bayou. Sometimes, the yellow, cup-like blooms unfold upon the surface.*

*From the deck of the house-
boat the opposite shore can
be seen behind streamers of
swaying moss.*

near the shore I heard the muted chirps and flutterings of red-
winged blackbirds as they chose roosting places for the coming
night, and from across the broad river came the call of a great
horned owl, eerie and primitive. Thoughtfully I walked back across
the island and climbed aboard the houseboat.

My afternoon's cruise down the twisting bayous and my short
excursion on the island had been fascinating in the extreme. After
supper I climbed to the top deck of the houseboat to enjoy the
solitude and the night sounds of river and forest, thrilled at the
sense of remoteness. This marshland has two separate and distinct
personalities. By day, under the blazing sun, its waters sparkle as if
set with a thousand gems and the trees along the bayous are mir-
rored in its surface. As night closes down and the full moon rises,
both marshland and the forest are transformed into a strange dark
world against a backdrop of starry skies. Soft breezes, blowing from
across the river, caress the face and carry the heavy scent of woodland blooms. Moss-draped trees that seemed very ordinary in daylight take on weird, grotesque shapes.

After the sun sinks behind The Island's forest, nocturnal creatures begin their period of daily activity.

On this night, the full moon was slowly rising above the forest across the river, making a moonpath over the water that undulated and shifted as currents slowly moved beneath the dark surface. As I sat watching the river I heard, now and then, the plop of striking fish and other sounds whose origins I could only guess at. From far overhead came the voices of migrating geese and I lifted my eyes to watch their broad V as it moved slowly southward. Following some built-in compass, the geese passed overhead, to merge, at last, with the rosy glow that still suffused the sky, leaving me with a sense of wonder as to their precise means of navigation. From the now-empty expanse above, my eyes dropped down to the river where a broad wedge-shaped wave moved slowly across the moon-swept river toward the opposite shore. Looking closely, I could see that it was created by some swimming animal with its head just above the surface. The animal swam diagonally across the river and disappeared into the fringing growth of tall marsh grass. No doubt I had seen an otter, since they are fairly common in this marshland.

As darkness increased, from everywhere around me came mysterious night sounds, rustlings, and buzzes. What caused the rustling sounds I do not know, but the hums and buzzes were the voices of katydids and crickets sawing out their nocturnal tunes. Bats circled over the river, now and then touching the surface, at other times flitting through the trees as they fed upon night-flying insects. They moved on silent wings and I heard no sound, but I knew that the bats were locating their prey by uttering high-pitched squeaks which were echoed off the insects' bodies and picked up by the bats' sensitive ears in a sonar-like technique called echo location. The bats darted among the trees, never touching a twig as they used this remarkable sense in navigation.

Truly, the night had a thousand voices but only a few could I identify. From far away in some hidden recess along a bayou came the deep, bass call of a bullfrog and from the edges of the forest I heard now and again the night songs of mockingbirds, low and muted as if the birds were singing in their sleep.

Slowly the moon climbed higher over the dark river and little by little the chirps of the crickets and katydids disappeared from the mingled sounds of the night. Suddenly I was startled by a brilliant flash and, looking upward, saw the glowing streak of a fireball crossing the sky. At first it was red, then changed to green and faded away at last over the forest.

These were the sights and the sounds of the marshland night, and as I climbed down the ladder to my bunk I reflected that here was a place where time stood still, where a thousand years or ten thousand years made little difference. Changes come to most places; forests are cleared and the land brought under cultivation to feed the expanding population; highways are built through wilderness areas making them so easily accessible that they are soon littered with discarded cans and bottles, the debris of civilization; cities and towns expand their boundaries, gradually overrunning the surrounding countrysides. By contrast, this vast savannah remains unaltered by the heavy hand of man, a place where the only visible changes were those brought about by the seasons. Here, I was to find, I could walk through an island forest or paddle my boat down some nameless bayou, seeing little to remind me that men had passed that way before.

Chapter 3

THE WORLD OF THE MARSH GRASS

WHILE CRUISING along the river and the bayous in the houseboat, I had viewed the marsh grass expanse from a distance, but I wished to see it at closer range, to study it in detail. During the days that followed, while my companions fished, I had opportunity to explore this vast, waving world of grass and to satisfy, in part, my curiosity concerning it.

We had towed several small boats behind the houseboat and I commandeered one of these for my purpose. Pulling away from the *Likilikit*, I paddled down the wide, slowly flowing river, remaining near the shore where the current often flowed upstream. It is a strange fact that near the shore of a meandering river there is often a counter current flowing in a direction opposite to that in the middle. This, of course, depends on the contour of the stream. Thus, even though I was going downstream, I was often forced to paddle against the current.

From the small boat, I had a much closer view of the marsh's edge. The grasses and reeds now towered far above my head, forming a green wall alongside which I slowly moved. Occasionally there were narrow openings where I could see deeper into the marsh, but it was not until I had paddled for some distance that I found, to my delight, a channel penetrating deeply into the grassy jungle. Into this narrow aisle I propelled my boat as far as possible, then sat quietly studying the strange green world which surrounded me. The recess into which I had pushed the boat consisted, I found,

of a solid stand of wild rice, its green stems reaching far above my head where each one was topped by a feathery panicle of blooms. From the tip of each slender branch was suspended a cluster of yellow, pollen-filled anthers which trembled in the passing breezes. Now and again bumblebees alighted and crawled among them, dusting their fuzzy bodies with the golden grains. Now and then they hovered in the air, as if suspended on invisible strings, while they employed their legs to brush the pollen from their bodies and concentrate it into pollen baskets on their hind legs. This done, they flew away toward The Island, where, no doubt, they had their colonies in old mouse nests. Honeybees, too, were busily harvesting the pollen and they, also, flew away toward The Island, perhaps to nests in hollow trees.

Through the green, waving stems of the tall marsh grasses I could glimpse colorful flowers pushing upward toward the light. There were twining morning-glories and mallows spreading their bright petals in the sun to entice flying insects. It was from these blooms that the bees obtained the nectar needed to supplement the pollen harvested from the grasses as food for their young. Grasses produce no nectar so bees must obtain this substance from other blooms. As I sat quietly studying the scene around me, I heard only the distant twittering of birds and the nearby, soft rustling of the grasses as their rough blades rasped against each other. I felt as if I were suspended in time, as if nothing existed beyond the range of my eyes. High overhead, fleecy clouds drifted along but this merely added to my illusion of complete isolation.

Out of the corner of my eye I noticed a movement on a grass blade, but when I looked again nothing was there. For a moment I was puzzled, but when I reached over and turned the leaf around I caught sight of a green, slant-faced grasshopper. As I slowly ro-

Top: *The grassy savannah stretches away to the horizon, interrupted here and there by hammock-like islands and lone cypresses. The marsh grasses often rise ten to twelve feet above the water.* Bottom: *Narrow channels snake away from the bayou at intervals. Although half-choked with fallen grass stems, they afford access into the deeper reaches of the marshland.*

tated the grass, the insect moved around to the opposite side. Quickly, I clasped my hand over the piece of grass and was successful in capturing the illusive creature, which turned out to be a *Leptysma* grasshopper, a Greek name meaning "slender." As the unhappy 'hopper struggled between my fingers I examined it more closely. Its body was very slender with a yellowish stripe extending back along each side of the body from eye to hind leg. Its face slanted backward, following the general contour of its body. *Leptysma* clings to the stems and blades of the marsh grasses, its body parallel to them and its long jumping legs folded beneath it. To the eye of a potential enemy, its form and coloration make it blend into the background upon which it rests. Its habit of dodging around behind the stem or leaf when danger threatens enables it to vanish as if by magic; now you see it and now you don't.

Where these marsh-inhabiting *Leptysmas* lay their eggs I do not know; presumably they are laid in the ground as is the habit of their relatives. Later I found them throughout the vast marshland, far from any solid ground, so one wonders how and where they find breeding sites. Through the summer days they perch quietly on the grasses and sedges, concerned not at all that winter's cold will one day invade their domain. As I held this specimen in my hand I could not help but ponder over the remarkable instincts that govern the lives of such insects, enabling them to locate solid ground when the time arrives for egg laying. This individual was a female and, barring capture by a bird or a frog, she would eventually mate and lay her eggs and, at last, be killed by the cold. Meanwhile, the *Leptysma* eggs would be protected in the earth and, with the arrival of another spring, would hatch into young 'hoppers. And so, future generations of *Leptysmas* would, I knew, continue to perch quietly upon the swaying stems of the marsh grasses in spite of storms and winter's cold. They would survive the years because the marshland does not change. I released my captive *Leptysma* and she hopped away, jumping from stem to stem. She, like the larger creatures of the marshland, had a date with destiny, however small and unimportant her place in the scheme of things.

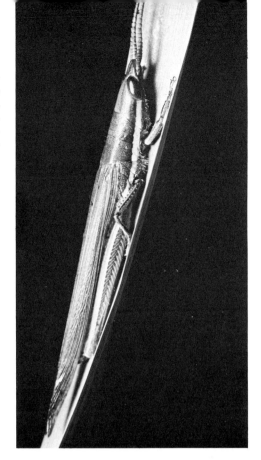

One of the most interesting of the marshland inhabitants is Leptysma, *a slender grasshopper that rests quietly upon the tall grasses. The form and coloration of its body camouflage it well.*

I continued my lonely vigil, hidden within the surrounding walls of green vegetation with only the sibilant rustlings of the grasses for company. Soon I was aware of a pair of golden eyes regarding me over the edge of a leaf. I sat quietly, my only movement being that imparted by the gently swaying boat. As I watched, a pair of green fingers reached over the edge of the leaf, then a bright green body came into view. It was, I realized, a green *Hyla* frog, a type of tree frog. Extending along its sides were rich, cream-colored stripes. It perched quietly upon the plant, but when I moved, it dodged around the leaf and disappeared, using the same evasive technique as the *Leptysma*. When I remained quiet, the *Hyla* frog peeked over the leaf again, then climbed slowly upward toward the grass blooms where numerous small flies were buzzing about in the sun.

One fly was so foolish as to alight near the frog. This was an error, since the frog's adhesive tongue flashed out and the fly was gone.

These *Hyla* frogs are common inhabitants of this vast marshland, well protected by their coats of vivid green as they rest upon the leaves. On their toes are expanded discs which enable them to crawl easily over the smooth surfaces of the vegetation. At night they vocalize by expanding their throats into thin resonance chambers and forcing air back and forth over their vocal cords. By day they stalk their insect game or, sometimes, swim through the water. But they are happiest when jewel-like drops of water hang suspended from the grass blades or when falling rain forms rivulets down their inner, V-shaped surfaces. In autumn, when fog drifts like a wet blanket over the marshland, their calls have muffled tones. In spring, they mate and lay their eggs in hidden pools where their tadpoles feed upon green algae and eventually grow into adult form. Even better adapted to life in the marsh than *Leptysma*, the *Hyla* frogs survive because they are fitted to the life they lead. In a sense, the marshland created the creatures that live there. They survive because they are adapted to its special conditions.

I had come to the marsh to enjoy its remoteness and quiet beauty, so I continued to sit quietly as the water beneath the towering grasses began to move almost imperceptibly toward the river. The tide was now running out and slowly draining the marsh. Looking upward through the network of grass blooms I saw, outlined against cottony clouds, the forms of two black vultures soaring aloft on motionless wings. Like ominous specters they circled the sky high above the waving sea of marsh grass. Their eyes, I knew, were searching for evidence of death, but they were in no hurry; the vultures could afford to be patient because death eventually comes to every marsh inhabitant, the large and the small. When it occurs, be it snake or muskrat, the birds drop down to feed. Upon the earth they are awkward and clumsy and they remain only long enough to devour what fate has provided. Their gruesome repast completed, they flap up again into their natural realm and sail once more on quiet wings. Sometimes, if their meal has been large, they

Left: A green tree frog of the marsh rests here on a pane of glass. The adhesive discs on its toes enable it to cling to any smooth surface, whether glass or grass stem. Right: Bullfrogs grow to large size in the marshland, feeding upon crayfish and even small snakes. At night, their booming voices echo across the grassy wilderness.

alight on bare cypress snags to permit the slow processes of digestion. While we may not appreciate the vultures' diet, in the marshland scheme they serve a useful purpose; they are scavengers who remove the carrion before it can contaminate the water or the land. Even as I watched, the two vultures circling above me began spiraling downward. Had their telescopic eyes seen evidence of death? As their dark forms disappeared behind the screening marsh grass I became aware of a loud splashing in the distance and I knew that some life and death struggle was taking place. Vultures do not expend their energies on useless investigation; they would without doubt garner the tidbits from some watery combat.

Looking down at the water I found that only a few inches now remained beneath the boat. The tide was flowing faster and numerous crabs which had been feeding in the marsh were retreating to deeper water. Even though this marshland is many miles from the Gulf, its tidal influence is felt here. Just as on the world's great seas and oceans where vast stretches of open water occur, the forces of lunar and solar gravities cause tidal ebbs and flows as the waters of the Gulf rise and fall. Since these tidal movements of the oceans have been occurring for untold eons it is, perhaps, not surprising that the creatures that dwell along or near their shores should be affected in one way or another. The tides come and go in recurring cycles that pass across succeeding days in an endless rhythm. Ocean waves result from the pressures of winds, but the tides result from cosmic forces; that is, from the gravitational pull exerted upon the fluid seas by both sun and moon. The pull of the moon is greater because it is nearer.

The Gulf of Mexico is partly surrounded by land, so its tidal fluctuations are usually slight, consisting only of gentle ebbs and flows. Still, they are sufficient to affect the marshland. Tidal rhythms are very complex, yet many animals that live in or near the sea have become adapted to them. Their instincts are atuned to the daily shifts of the tides; in fact, their survival depends upon their ability to fit their daily lives into the local tidal cycles. The grasses that wave above the wet lands of the marsh are probably but little affected; their roots grow deeply enough into the black muck to assure sufficient moisture regardless of the tidal fluctuations. The river with its fresh water pushes downward away from the land, holding back the salt water for a time. Then, when tides rise, the sea again flows into the marsh in an eternal seesaw contest between fresh and salt water.

While I daydreamed in my hidden retreat among the marsh plants, the tide continued to recede and at last patches of mud and sand appeared above the water. Over these exposed areas, fiddler crabs scurried about as if in a great hurry to do whatever it is that fiddler crabs do. Some of them burrowed into the mud while others appeared to be feeding. These ubiquitous little crustaceans have an unusual characteristic: one claw of the male is greatly enlarged while the other is very small. Either the right or the left claw may be the larger and it is held across the front of the crab. When in the presence of the female, the male waves its large claw back and forth

Above: *Fiddler crabs scurry about beneath the growth of tall marsh grass.*

In close-up, the enormous size of a fiddler's enlarged claw can be seen. The other claw is very small. Because of their habit of waving this large claw about, they are called fiddlers.

in a manner suggesting a violinist in action. It is because of this habit that they are called fiddler crabs. These little crabs undergo certain color changes which are closely related to the shifting tides and to the time of day. During daylight hours and during periods of low tides the crabs become darker in color. It is at this time, too, that they are most active. They come out of their burrows and scurry over the sand or mud among the marsh grasses, feeding upon whatever the tide has left. When darkness settles, they fade to paler shades of yellowish white. These changes in hue are the result of the expansion and contraction of dark pigment cells in their outer covering. When these pigment cells expand, the fiddler becomes darker in color.

What useful purpose do these color changes serve? Certainly they must benefit the little creatures in some way or they would never have appeared during the long period of fiddler crab evolution. Nor would they be so perfectly timed as to coincide with the natural phenomena of the marsh if some benefit were not derived. It is possible that the darker color assumed during the day helps to camouflage them from enemies; on the other hand, it may be that the color changes are helpful in regulating the temperature of their bodies. They, like all crabs, are "cold-blooded;" that is, their body temperature tends to be the same as that of their surroundings. At any event, the biological clocks contained within their bodies are "set" to follow the tidal rhythms and, even when taken away from their native habitat and kept under constant laboratory conditions, their color changes and periods of increased activity continue to follow the tidal rhythms of the coast where they are native. The darkening of their color tends to occur about fifty-six minutes later each twenty-four-hour period; it corresponds to the daily shift of the tidal cycle. If the crabs are collected on a coast where two high tides occur each day, their color and activity cycles tend to correspond to the two high tides of the lunar day. Thus are the marshland and inhabitants influenced by great cosmic forces from beyond the confines of earth, an influence that extends not only to the rise and fall of the tides but even to the colors of the small fiddler crabs that dwell there.

Eventually I was forced by the receding water to push my boat out of the marsh. This I did with some difficulty, but, once free of the mud, I paddled on down along the shore, studying the vegetation as I went. Once I saw a rail forcing its way through the dense growth of grasses, its thin body admirably adapted to squeezing between the stems. I thought of the old cliché, "thin as a rail," a most apt expression.

The tall feathery plumes of wild rice are visited by bumblebees seeking pollen. Nectar is gathered from flowers growing here and there in the marsh.

The river margin was fringed by tall marsh grasses of several kinds; there were growths of giant foxtail or *Setaria* grass, also known as "jungle millet." Its stems reached nearly twelve feet above the water, each one topped by a feathery plume. Occasionally I passed patches of tall reeds or Phragmites, as well as wild rice or *Zizania*. All these tall grasses swayed gently in the breeze, adding grace and beauty to the vista of sky and water.

Pausing at several points, I used my knife to cut the stems of these grasses to examine their inner structure. I was interested in determining, if possible, how such slender stems could support the tall plants in the high winds which often sweep across the marshland, bending down the vegetation. After such winds, the marsh grasses, slender and weak as they appear, always rise up again unharmed.

Sometimes, in late summer, hurricanes, bred in tropical seas to the south, scream across these lowlands. The great cyclonic storms, often hundreds of miles in diameter, rotate counterclockwise and their winds often reach 150 miles per hour. Before a hurricane, there is a time of suspense when slowly rising waters seeth inward

through the marsh and when frigate birds and other winged creatures of the open sea fly landward before the coming gale. The
birds soar on restless wings beneath clouds racing across the sky
from east to west. Gusts of wind caress the tall grasses and move
across their swaying tops like unseen hands. As the eye of the hurricane moves relentlessly closer, the waters continue to rise, pushing
farther and farther into the marsh. Soon the sea birds are gone and
the winds increase, blowing with ever greater intensity. Always
they blow from the east while the hurricane is still to the south over
the warm waters of the Gulf whence it draws its energy to live.
Nearer and nearer it comes, traveling no faster than a slow-moving
automobile. Yet, the rotary winds around its eye spin at amazing
speeds, whipping the salty Gulf beneath it into a confused mass of
angry waves and seething foam. In time, it roars upon the coast
where tall cypresses and live oaks bend and often snap like match-
sticks. Winds of fantastic speeds sweep across the marsh, bending
the grasses flat against the water. The wild inhabitants of the marshland and the islands seek refuge wherever they can find it. Those
that can fly or swim have mostly gone inland, warned, perhaps, by
some unknown instinct. Snakes swim to higher bits of land, the
poisonous kinds forming hazards to any man so unfortunate as to
have sought refuge there.

And so the hours pass while the winds of the hurricane continue
to blow, still from the east. At last the gale suddenly dies away and
the lashing waters become strangely quiet, their surfaces glassy. A
dead calm now settles over the marshland, but it is an uneasy calm
and the waters are still far above their normal level; only an occasional gust ripples the surface. The center of the storm has arrived,
the quiet eye about which the great winds pivot.

The hush that settles over the marsh is punctuated now and
again by the tentative call of a bird or the gentle rustle of the
grasses. High overhead, scudding cloud fragments move across the
sky against a blue-gray background. Low around the distant horizon hangs a black curtain of storm clouds, illuminated at intervals
by lightning flashes, deep red and menacing. Time seems to have

The edges of the marsh grasses are set with sharp teeth, as can be seen under magnification. This grass can easily cut the flesh like a knife.

Below left: When a marsh grass stem is cut lengthwise it can be seen that there are divisions, or septa, extending crosswise. Such structure gives it strength and resilience.

Below right: The stems of the tall rushes are strengthened by being composed of numerous cylinders, all attached together. This assures great strength along with little weight, and the marsh vegetation can bend under the force of high winds without breaking.

come to a halt and to be waiting; even the voices of the few birds
are hushed as if in fear or uncertainty. Some sixth sense, perhaps,
tells them that the eye, like the rest of the great storm, is moving
inland and that the winds will come again. Soon its southern edge
arrives and the winds commence to blow once more, but they have
now reversed themselves and blow from the west. Trees and plants
that withstood the easterly winds are now bent in the opposite direction. Eventually, of course, the hurricane will die upon the land,
no longer energized by heat from the warm seas and gradually los-
ing its power through friction against the land over which it moves.
Thus is the tropical hurricane born and thus it eventually dies, but
it leaves desolation behind it as a grim reminder of its fury. Great
trees lie prostrate upon the islands and others have broken limbs,
but the tall marsh grasses gradually straighten up again, for the
most part unharmed by the winds that bent them down.

I solved the question of the grasses' strength, at least to my own
satisfaction. I found by cutting the stems of the various tall marsh
grasses that all had one thing in common; instead of being solid
like a tree trunk, they are made up of numerous hollow, cylindrical
or rectangular tubes closely attached together. As any engineer
knows, a hollow cylinder or a square tube resists bending much
better than a solid rod having the same amount of structural material. A sheet of stiff paper will support but little weight, yet when
rolled into a cylinder it can support several pounds. Being constructed in this fashion, the grass stems may grow to relatively
great heights and support heavy blooms or seed clusters at their
tops. Thus, the reeds and grasses that wave so gracefully along the
river and the bayous can bend without breaking under the force of
the hurricane's winds. Their secret lies in their ability to "give"
with the wind, not to resist it.

The marsh vegetation that thrives here exists in a tension zone
where salt and fresh waters often intermingle; they can grow in
water that is often quite salty. The same is true of the cypresses and
some other trees that flourish along the bayous. In these waters
there are also abundant growths of marine algae that we normally

Large sturgeons are common in the river where they feed on the bottom by means of sucker-like mouths. Some kinds spend part of their lives in the sea.

think of as living only in the sea.

The marshland is truly a world apart. Its plants and animals live under very special conditions imposed by an unstable habitat of moving water and, sometimes, of violent winds. It is a place where very special adaptations, indeed, are a necessity.

At one point on my river expedition, I rounded a bend and saw a man hauling in a large fish. Naturally I was interested, so I pulled in closer to see what it was. The fish in question was a five-foot sturgeon that had been captured in a wire-mesh trap baited with chicken viscera, the usual bait for catfish. This was the first sturgeon I had seen from these waters, though I was aware of their presence and later saw an eight-foot specimen.

Sturgeons are ganoid fishes and so are rather closely related to the gars, but, unlike the gars, their bodies are not completely encased in body scales. There are five rows of large plate-like scales extending along the body and, instead of jaws armed with sharp teeth, the mouth is in the form of a ventral sucking organ. Sturgeons occur in many of the world's great river systems, where they often grow to enormous size, some reaching lengths of nearly twenty

Left: *The pastel shades of the marshland are brightened, here and there, by scarlet cardinal flowers, which are visited by bees.* Right: *Hidden deep among the marsh grasses, pink blooms of mallows add splashes of color.*

feet. The common sturgeon of the local bayous and the river lives most of its life in the sea, returning to fresh water only to lay its eggs. It ascends to the limits of tide water and deposits its eggs, often as many as three million. These are heavier than the water and sink, adhering to bottom materials. In time, the young return to their ancient home in the sea, where they remain until the urge to lay eggs stimulates them to run up the rivers. Sturgeons of other kinds live out their entire lives in fresh water, having divorced themselves completely from the sea.

The sturgeons are "suckers." They feed on the bottoms of the rivers and the bayous by means of their tubular mouths, which they extend like vacuum cleaners to suck up whatever food is available. Beneath their snouts are sensitive barbels which drag along the bottom; when food is located by these sensory organs, the tubular mouth is extended and the food is quickly sucked in. Thus, these great fishes cruise along over the bottom, feeding as they go.

As the Pascagoula meanders southward to unite its waters at last with those of the Gulf, it passes alternately between forested banks and vast stretches of open savannah. I had explored in some detail the grassy marsh below The Island, so on a later afternoon I extended by investigations farther afield. Some distance above The Island, the river makes a sharp bend and, after several miles, almost meets itself. In fact, only a narrow neck of land separates the channels as they approach each other and, from a boat, one can see the other portion of the river through the trees. It is somewhat discouraging to paddle for several hours against the current on a hot day and then to realize that one has arrived back at a point only a few hundred feet away. But meandering rivers are like that; the early voyageurs, to whom rivers were the only highways, often had to travel long distances to arrive at nearby destinations.

Enclosed within this particular loop of the river is a low marsh, as usual covered with tall grasses and reeds. At one point, a narrow channel opens into this isolated marshland. I discovered it only by accident, since, when seen from the river, its entrance is hidden behind the grassy wall. Into this channel I paddled my boat and was pleased to find that the water meandered on into the depths of the marsh and that its width averaged about five feet, permitting easy access. These channels are almost always of uniform width and quite deep, kept scoured out by the tidal movements of the water flowing in and out in a recurring rhythm. Overhead, the grasses almost meet, so that the channels are more like green tunnels. After nearly a quarter of a mile, the twisting route suddenly opened out into a large circular pool along one side of which rose a muddy bank. As I approached this opening I was startled by a loud splashing and a beating of wings and saw half a dozen ducks rising into the air. Quacking in protest, they flew away across the marsh and silence reigned again.

At the opposite side of the pond I noticed an opening. Paddling my boat into it, I found that it continued deeper into the jungle of giant grasses. A few hundred feet farther on, I was somewhat disturbed to discover that the channel divided into several branches, each leading away in a different direction. I realized that a person could easily become confused and lost in this labyrinth. Too, I experienced a rising feeling of claustrophobia brought on by the impenetrable green walls of grass that seemed to close in on me. However, believing that I could orient myself by the sun, which was visible in the west, I paddled on into the savannah, occasionally stopping to examine plants or to collect insect specimens. Several times I saw cottonmouth moccasins on the mudbanks, but they paid me little heed. Once I surprised a small alligator. Otherwise, animal life of larger forms seemed absent and I was on the point of turning the boat around and retracing my path, if a wide enough place in the channel could be found. Suddenly, far ahead, where the watery aisle curved toward the right, I saw an animal swimming in the water. Apparently it had not seen me and, as it swam along down the channel away from me, I could see that its tail was used as combination swimming and steering organ. This, plus its brown coloration, identified it as a muskrat. I followed as it disappeared around the bend and shortly came to a large muskrat house completely blocking the channel. It was about six feet in diameter, oval in shape, and its top was at least two feet above the water. There were no extrances visible but these, I knew, were hidden below the water's surface. Such muskrat houses are built by the adult animals with a great amount of toil and consist of grass stems gathered in the vicinity and dragged atop the heap.

After pushing the bow of the boat onto the house, I stepped out and found that it supported my weight. Since I was curious as to the interior architecture of such a muskrat house I returned to the boat for my machete and began cutting and digging. After removing dried and matted grasses to a depth of a foot or so, I encountered the first chamber or den. It was a foot in diameter and lined with soft grasses, some of which were still green, an indication of recent construction and habitation. Further excavation revealed several similar chambers, all connected by passages. It is in these chambers that the muskrats live and rear their rat-like young, but no young were present this late in the season. The muskrat is, in

Scattered along the bayous are muskrat kitchen-middens strewn with the scattered clam shells. Muskrats open the shells to eat the contained mollusks.

many ways, a miniature beaver and its house is quite similar; but whereas the muskrat uses grasses and bulrushes as structural material, the beaver uses sticks. I think it was Ernest Thompson Seton, the great naturalist, who called the muskrat "the beaver's little brother."

These houses are ideally suited to occupancy by the aquatic rodents; they take advantage of a readily available source of building material and their homes are, in effect, air-conditioned. Matted grass is an excellent insulating agent, so the houses are cool in summer and warm in winter. I recalled the palm-thatched huts of the Pacific Islanders, which, even at tropical midday, are always cool. While the muskrats occupy these dome-shaped houses all year, it is during early summer that the young are born, at which time the males are driven from home and not allowed to return until the young are able to seek their own food.

My investigations of the muskrat house had taken considerable time but I had been unaware of its passing. Suddenly I realized that the sun had disappeared behind the marsh grass and that it would soon be dark. Already I could hear the typical sounds of dusk, the fluttering of birds in the grasses and the evening calls of frogs and crickets. From high overhead a nighthawk dropped down out of the darkening sky, its wings vibrating from the speed of its dive. Hurriedly I pushed the boat off and was gratified to find that there was sufficient space to turn it around. I had now lost all interest in biological investigations; my only desire was in getting out of the marsh before darkness. Paddling the boat as fast as possible along the channel, I at last came to a fork and took the one to the right. The grassy "tunnels" all looked alike but I was confident that I had chosen the correct one. However, the darkness was rapidly increasing and I had no desire to spend the night here in the marsh. Actually, there would be no physical danger, yet, with my active imagination, I could think of all sorts of possible happenings because, in truth, these vast savannahs are lonely and mysterious places even during the daylight hours.

Just beyond a sharp bend, the channel ended abruptly against a wall of tall jungle millet and I experienced an acute sense of fright. Pushing the boat's bow into the shallow water at the channel's edge, I climbed out and successfully maneuvered it around. Now I was really concerned and could no longer deceive myself into believing otherwise. It had become so dark that I could see but a few yards ahead. To add fuel to my fears, there came a loud splash from some hidden pool in the marsh to my left and this spurred me to even greater efforts at paddling. There is no greater stimulus to fear than that of running and this, of course, was what I was doing.

After what seemed hours but which was probably only a few minutes, I arrived back at the fork where I had taken the wrong turn. With rising confidence I now paddled on down what I believed to be the correct channel but which was now merely a dark passage between high walls. A few stars were visible overhead and darkness had definitely settled over the grassy world through which I moved. At this point I noticed a greenish phosphorescence glowing along the channel's margins. It helped not at all for me to remind myself that this was interesting biologically, being caused by luminous molds or bacteria growing on dead organic matter. As my paddle dug furiously into the water I could even visualize clearly the headlines which would appear in the local papers; "Body of Biologist Found in Pascagoula Swamp, Had Been Missing for Several Days." I even wondered hopefully if they might say, "Well-Known Biologist," but decided that this was being too optimistic.

I was now paddling the boat by guess; only vaguely could I see the walls of grass fringing the channel. Abruptly, the bow bumped into yielding mud and stuck there. Back-paddling frantically, I was soon able to extricate it and move on. Apparently I had run aground, or rather "a-mud," at a sharp bend and from then

Great blue herons stalk minnows and frogs along the edges of the bayous, sailing away on outspread wings when danger threatens.

Among the more attractive marsh plants are the arrow-leafed morning-glories (Ipomoea sagittata) that climb among the tall grasses. In summer, the pale blue flowers glow like stars hidden in the green vegetation. This specimen was photographed in autumn after the blooms had withered.

on the channel seemed straight. After a few hundred feet I finally came to another bend and, to my great relief, found it to be the curved entrance to the river.

Freed from the enclosing walls of giant grasses—which had seemed twice as tall in the darkness— I found that the full moon was rising over the opposite shore, illuminating the river with its soft yellow glow. Pausing for a moment, I lighted a cigarette and allowed my nerves to settle, then paddled the boat out into the slowly moving current which carried me downstream. Once I was out of the marsh my fears subsided and now seemed foolish, but they were very real at the time. Soon, after rounding a long curve, I spotted the lights of the *Likilikit* near the far shore against the dark trees of The Island. This marshland is, indeed, a fascinating place to explore alone—in daylight, that is.

After tying up the small boat I climbed aboard the houseboat and found my companions engrossed in a poker game. Not being particularly proud of my panic while in the marsh I failed to mention it, telling them only that I had found so many interesting things that I had been delayed. This, of course, was true as far as it went.

While in the field, a biologist's work is never finished. At night while others may relax in drowsy conversation or at playing cards, a biologist must preserve his specimens or photograph them; otherwise his work is wasted. I had been interested in the marsh grasses and in their structural adaptations for survival in the winds that often sweep across these low savannahs. I had collected a number of the grass stems and now set up close-up equipment to photograph them by electronic flash. This done, I then developed the films to make sure the negatives would make satisfactory prints. This is a habit of long standing. It can be very disappointing to delay film development until returning to the studio, only to find that exposures were wrong or that some unknown malfunction had occurred in the cameras or flash rigs. I learned this the hard way; once I traveled two thousand miles and waited until my return to process the films, only to find that a camera shutter had been defective almost from the beginning.

Later, in my bunk, I lay listening to the gentle lapping of the river against the shore and against the great cypresses along its margin. The boat slowly swung about in the current, now and then grating softly against the cypress knees. Lulled to sleep at last, I dreamed of being lost far underground in an unexplored cave where the endless, dark passages led to nowhere.

Chapter 4

THE TREE

THE FIRST HUNTER to perch in a *machan* or platform in a jungle tree, awaiting a tiger's return to its kill, had an idea that can be used with great success by a naturalist. I do not know exactly what sort of psychology is involved, but apparently ground-living animals do not expect humans to inhabit trees and so a person may usually sit quietly in a tree and observe them going about their daily routines in a normal manner.

There is a small stream that meanders across the western end of The Island. Technically it is not really a stream since it is connected with the surrounding water at each end and its flow is intermittent, being governed by rising and falling of the tides; sometimes it flows in one direction and sometimes in the other. One bank is high and steep, with exposed tree roots hanging down over it, groping for anchorage. The other bank is sloping and set with a dense growth of tall cane. The cane resembles tropical bamboo and is, in truth, merely a smaller variety of it.

At one point along this stream there grows a large live oak, its great moss-draped branches extending out over the bed of the stream as if to conceal it from the sky. The branches are crooked and twisted and follow no pattern, but there is a place, about fifteen feet from the ground, where several branches, more than a foot through, snake away from the gnarled trunk forming a comfortable perch where I have a ringside seat to the forest goings-on.

This morning, with pencil and clipboard, I climbed to this obser-

A perch in a large live oak near The Island's center affords a view of the forest floor. Most wild creatures ignore a man hidden in a tree high above the ground. The water-filled cavity or "tree hole," right, contains aquatic insects of several kinds.

vation post and made myself comfortable. Here I sit, among the branches of the great, sprawling tree while the hot semitropical sun beats down upon the green canopy high above. In the shade where I perch it is cool, since the green chlorophyll in the leaves absorbs much of the sun's energy, using it to manufacture starch and sugar. As I look around I see only the gentle movement of the leaves and the rhythmic swaying of vines and moss, yet I know that I am seated at the center of one of the world's great and amazing factories. Within the tissues of the oak are endless veins and tubes carrying water and food materials. Deep within its trunk is the xylem or woody zone through which water and dissolved minerals are flowing upward from the roots deeply buried in The Island's loam. Nearer the surface, just beneath the bark, lie ducts filled with sugars and other foods, all flowing slowly down from manufacturing centers in the sun-washed leaves. This great factory is silent,

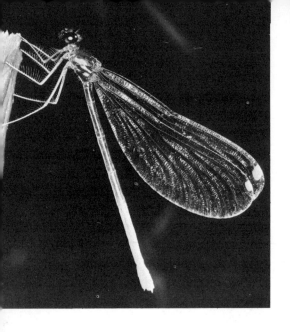

Left: *A black-winged damselfly alights on a twig, now and then darting away to capture flying insects in a basket formed by its spiny legs.* Above: *Strewn along the stream bed are the wings of black damselflies (Agrion), evidence that some bird has dined.*

yet it pulses with an astonishing vitality as its living processes ebb and flow with the passing of the nights and the days. From every limb and twig hang the long streamers of Spanish moss, gray in color and adding a strange, exotic touch to the great tree. Spanish moss is not really a moss at all but an air plant related to pineapple and to the flowering bromeliads that festoon so many trees in the Everglades of Florida. Known to botanists as *Tillandsia usneoides*, it is not a parasite and obtains no food directly from the tree upon which it grows. Yet it can live only upon a tree, since it absorbs its needed minerals from dust washed off the tree's leaves by rainwater.

Seemingly, Spanish moss exists on nothing, but actually this is not so. If a strand of this strange air plant is examined under a lens it appears scaly or scurfy, an adaptation for catching and holding the particles of dust and the moisture it needs to live. Requiring high humidity, it thrives only in warm, damp places such as the coastal zones of southeastern United States. When removed from these moisture-laden areas it quickly dies.

As I sit ruminating over the wonders of the great tree, I glance down now and again to the stream and its bordering jungle. Usually, there is little to be seen except the clear water flowing along over its sandy bed. Patches of sunlight move slowly back and forth as the branches far above sway gently in the air. Flitting about over the water and along its margins are Agrions, or black-winged damselflies, the metallic-green bodies of the males glowing with bright iridescence as they pass through shafts of sunlight. The more somber hued females perch sedately upon plants just above the water. On a patch of bare sand I notice four black damselfly wings scattered about like fallen leaves, evidence that some woodland bird has dined. On a nearby leaf, only a yard away, a strange insect alights. Little over an inch in length, it is winged and holds its tail over its back like a scorpion; its mouthparts are elongated into beak-like form. I identify the insect as a male scorpionfly, an insect with an ancient lineage. The fossilized remains of its remote ancestors have been found, I recall, in Triassic beds many millions of years old. The females lay their eggs on the ground where the caterpillar-like young feed on dead insects.

I am convinced that if I watch the forest floor long enough and have patience enough, something interesting is bound to happen, so

A scorpionfly alights on a vine, its scorpion-like tail held over its back. There is no sting in the tail, however; the insect is completely harmless.

I continue my vigil and at last am rewarded by the sight of some animal moving quietly among the green cane stems. At first I think my eyes have deceived me but still I watch and, after a minute or so, a swamp rabbit hops out on a sandbar. For a moment it freezes, then jumps into the water and walks along in a very unrabbit-like manner. Its huge chocolate-margined ears are erect for any sound and its eyes watch the surrounding vegetation for danger, but it fails to see me in my unique location. After several minutes the rabbit leaves the water and leaps to the top of a stump where it can see in all directions. It looks up and down the stream—but not overhead. This is evidently its favorite observation post since many rabbit droppings are present on the stump's flat top, evidence of past visits. The rabbit sits very still and I soon tire of watching him; my eyes wander away in search of other things. A tree leaf suddenly sways rapidly back and forth but the motion, I decide, is merely the result of a stray breeze. Still the rabbit sits quietly. A rabbit has plenty of time; with abundant, leafy food everywhere it need not search for nourishment. Soon, however, it leaves the stump and disappears among the canes.

Why, I wonder, did the rabbit walk along in the stream bed instead of the dry bank? Perhaps we have here a survival instinct; a rabbit is almost completely defenseless and so must avoid its enemies by strategy. The flowing water obliterates its scent trail and a predator which may be following will be confused. These swamp rabbits, sometimes called cane cutters, are common throughout the marshland and low forested areas and I am always astonished at their abundance. Their scientific name, *Sylvilagus aquaticus*, is most appropriate since the specific name, *aquaticus*, means "of the water." While its smaller cousin, the cottontail, inhabits the drier fields and brush patches, the swamp rabbit is a denizen of the deep swamps and river bottoms and almost never strays far from water; I have often seen them swimming across wide rivers. When alarmed they almost always take to the nearest stream, apparently using this ruse to destroy their scent and thus evade pursuers.

I am interrupted at this point in my reflections on rabbits by a

Carolina wren that has spied me and sets up a loud fuss from a twig only a few feet away. The wren is most unhappy at this intrusion on its private domain and emphatically tells me its views on the matter. But after a few minutes it apparently decides that nothing is.being accomplished by the scolding, so flies off to another twig and begins hunting bugs. However, the wren's reproving voice has been heard by two jays, and since no jay can long ignore a woodland quarrel, they fly over to investigate. They look me over carefully but, apparently deciding that I am not especially intriguing, fly off to more interesting things. I realize, of course, that if I had been an owl they would have raised such a hubbub that all the birds on The Island would have been attracted like iron filings to a magnet. It is not particularly flattering to know that I rate less applause than an owl but, since I desire peace and quiet, I am satisfied.

Overhead, a few scattered clouds drift across the sky, seen now and then through the screening foliage and moss. Below me, on the surface of the stream, a group of small water striders skips rapidly about, creating ripples on the otherwise quiet surface. Suddenly my attention is attracted by a butterfly fluttering about near the base of a nearby tree where I previously noticed sap flowing from a break in the bark. This sap, apparently fermenting, has attracted a large assemblage of insects, including moths, butterflies, ants, and wasps. However, there is something unusual about the actions of the butterfly I have just noticed, so I laboriously climb down from my perch in the live oak to investigate. Approaching cautiously, I am surprised to see that it is a brown goatweed butterfly and that it is attempting to escape from a large, black carpenter ant whose jaws are fastened to one of its hind wings. The ant hangs on like a tiny terrier while the butterfly flutters its wings in futile efforts to escape.

Hurrying back to the base of the live oak I obtain my camera and am successful in snapping a picture of the little woodland drama. Then, as I watch, the butterfly continues its struggles, sometimes dragging the ant along for an inch or so. I am concerned since, somehow, it seems unfair that an attractive butterfly should

be killed by an ant. However, my concern is needless. The butterfly suddenly beats its wings and flies away with the ant still hanging on. Once airborne, it moves with ease and quickly disappears
from view among the trees.

How this contest finally terminated, I have no way of knowing,
but I do recall having once captured a May beetle with an ant's
jaws still clamped to one of its hind legs. The ant's head had been
severed or broken from its body, leaving jaws and head attached.
In the case of the goatweed butterfly, I am mystified as to how the
ant had been able to clamp its jaws onto the hind wing in the first
place; butterflies are usually very alert and agile. I can only conclude that the butterfly's senses had probably been dulled by im-
bibing fermented sap and so the aggressive ant had been able to
seize its wing.

Once again in my perch in the tree, I settle down and soon notice
a snake making its way by slow undulations along the bank of the
stream. At this point, I am interrupted by the return of the wren,
now with its beak full of insects. This seems strange, so I watch it
with renewed interest. The small brown bird now seems even more
disturbed by my presence than previously, which makes me suspect

A black carpenter ant seizes the hind wing of a goat-weed butterfly as it sips fer-mented sap from a tree. Even-tually, the butterfly is able to fly away with ant still hold-ing onto its wing.

that she has a nest in the vicinity. Wrens, I know, do not build exposed nests so I am at a loss to explain her actions. Standing up on my precarious perch, I examine the trunk and surrounding limbs for cavities but, since none is seen, I sit down again. Still the wren continues to hop about from twig to twig with a great fluttering of wings. I am so mystified that I decide that further investigation is necessary, especially when she finally sets up an angry chattering. Looking around on the opposite side of the trunk I at last find a large tree hole and, inside, four fuzzy young. This solves the mystery, but what am I to do now? There is no other perch nearby and I am not yet ready to leave. Finally, I decide that she will just have to get used to my presence if her young are to be fed. Fortunately, after another half hour's chattering and fluttering about, she eventually decides to take a chance and feed her nestlings. My conscience now relieved, I settle down once more to watch the stream and the surrounding forest floor.

The sun has climbed higher in the sky and beats down with even greater intensity. From far overhead, the monotonous cicada chorus filters down, periodically rising in volume, then fading away again. This, I know, is their time in the sun. For many years they lived beneath the ground feeding upon the sap of tree roots, their lives timed precisely by the seasons. At long last they were alerted, by some little-understood stimulus, to creep up out of their dark cells; the biological clocks within their bodies have informed them that the time has arrived to acquire wings, to mate and sing in the sun. Cicadas are strange insects with strange habits; they are closely related to the tiny aphids or plant lice which often live on our flowers or garden plants, sucking sap from their stems. Cicadas of some kinds live for long periods beneath the ground; the seventeen-year cicada, for instance, requires that interval for its subterranean development. Sometimes they are called locusts but this is incorrect since true locusts belong to the grasshopper family. But unlike katydids and crickets, cicadas do not "sing" by sawing one body part against another; their songs are made by means of vibrating drumheads. Above me The Island's cicadas sound their drums until my ears are almost deafened; the sound has a timeless quality and I know that cicadas will still be singing a million years in the future because insects and their habits change but slowly.

Below me, the stream flows along, its surface disturbed here and there by the gyrations of whirligig beetles. From previous close-up examinations, I know that these beetles have their eyes divided so that their upper parts see above the water and their lower parts below the water. Thus, they are amazingly adapted to the lives they live on the water's surface film. In one deep, clear pool a large crawfish moves slowly along searching for food. All is quiet. Then suddenly I notice a disturbance in the vegetation on the stream's high bank where it appears that some animal is slowly moving along. At first it is difficult to determine what the creature is, then a head pushes out from among the weeds and I see a black band like a robber's mask extending across a furry face. Two inquisitive eyes search the stream, then the 'coon—for that is what it is—shuffles down the bank. Without looking to right or left it peers intently into the water for a moment, then begins fishing about with its paws. I assume it is dabbling for crawfish but its luck is poor so it moves slowly on down the streambed and disappears. 'Coons are common throughout this vast marshland, even beyond the last forested areas toward the coast. We usually think of these animals as being denizens of forests but they have adapted themselves to the realm of marsh and grass and open sky all the way to the open Gulf.

I am always fascinated by the generic name of the raccoon, *Procyon*, from the star of the same name which rises just before the Dog Star. Perhaps this is in allusion to a fancied resemblance of the raccoon to members of the dog family. *Procyon* is derived from two Greek words, *pro*, meaning "before," and *cyon*, meaning "dog." The complete scientific name of this interesting mammal is *Procyon lotor*. *Lotor* is of Latin origin meaning "one who washes." 'Coons almost always attempt to wash their food in water before eating it.

It is surprising to find what we ordinarily think of as forest-loving animals, such as 'coons, living in open marshland and I find myself comparing my island and the surrounding area to other marshlands I have known. All have certain similarities as well as certain differences. Bears, for example, occur in the Everglades of Florida, but, of course, this vast sea of grass is interspersed with forested hammocks and, near the coasts, large tracts of mangroves. The word hammock, by the way, is of Seminole origin meaning "a garden place." It was on these bits of high ground that the Florida Indians lived and gardened.

As I sit pondering over the presence of forest-living creatures here on my island, I recall past trips deep into the Everglades, the world's largest and most amazing marshland. The early Spanish cartographers labeled it "El Laguno del Espiritu Santo" but in the early 1700's an English surveyor named Gerard de Brahm called this strange watery expanse the "River Glades." "Glade" or "glaed" is an old British word meaning "an open grassy place in a forest." By some strange twist, later maps changed the name to Everglades. In many respects, the Pascagoula Swamp resembles the Everglades with its forested hammocks spotted here and there in a grassy expanse. In truth, the Everglade hammocks are islands, which from a distance appear to be mere clumps of cabbage palms and other trees. Only when one penetrates into the interior of a hammock, however, is its true nature evident. When the explorer of one of these strange islands pushes through the surrounding wall of dense vegetation he enters an eerie realm of semi-gloom where the earth is black and bare of all plant life except the trunks of the trees which tower upward and expand into an interlaced network of leaf-covered branches far above. The trees are cajeput, mahogany, gumbo limbo, live oak, and palm, their trunks, here and there, decorated with epiphytic ferns, mosses, and orchids, the blooms of the latter adding bright touches of color. But these hammocks are, in truth, islets separated from the continental land mass just as my island is separated from the higher ground. I recall, too, still other such places I have visited and, in my mind's eye, I picture palm-fringed atolls set down in the South Pacific. I see snow-white beaches where breakers roll endlessly over the reefs and I feel again the crunch of sand beneath my bare feet and hear the trade wind in the palm fronds. All these bits of land are islands, yet how different they are from each other and from my present island.

As my pencil scratches across the paper recording my thoughts, I am suddenly recalled to the present by a loud fluttering of wings in a clump of buttonbushes below. Looking down I see a pigeon hawk perched about two feet from the ground. I am mystified until I notice a sparrow huddled upon the dry leaves beneath the hawk. Both birds are completely motionless. The hawk had evidently chased the sparrow down through the bushes but missed its mark, and the sparrow is now frozen upon the leafy floor of the forest. This is an interesting little tableau and I wonder what will happen next. Why does the sparrow not attempt an escape while the hawk is at rest above it? Why does the hawk not strike at the sparrow? At least ten minutes pass and the tension builds up, but neither bird makes a move. I am more and more puzzled and wonder how this drama will end. What I am seeing is a battle of wits with the sparrow's life at stake. Several more minutes pass, then suddenly the hawk strikes at the sparrow. But the sparrow darts away in time and escapes. Now, at last, I have time to re-enact the episode in my mind and to try to understand the actions of each bird. Once the hawk had missed its mark it was apparently at a disadvantage since the sparrow was upon the ground and alert to any movement made by the hawk in the bush above it. From then on it was a waiting game and the sparrow eventually took the initiative and darted away. Thus did I interpret the little play of life, but, as always, a human cannot know what actually goes on in the brains of wild creatures.

In spite of the fact that my perch in the oak is not particularly comfortable, the time has passed rapidly and I now find that it is midday and I am hungry. Fortunately I brought a lunch along so I begin eating, tossing bread crusts to the earth beside the stream. As expected, these tidbits soon attract several small birds, apparently sparrows, that seize them in their beaks and fly off.

The sun is now almost directly overhead and a midday lull

settles over both the tree and the surrounding forest; even the cicadas have muffled their drums. Gradually I become aware of a rustling sound apparently originating in dry leaves beneath a dense clump of shrubby bushes but, from my elevated position, I cannot see the cause so I wait quietly, hoping for a glimpse of whatever it is. After a minute or so a brown thrasher hops out into the open and begins scratching away the fallen leaves. First it scratches, then backs up to see if anything of an edible nature has been exposed, and then repeats the performance. I am strongly reminded of domestic hens I have seen doing the same thing. Thrashers are related to the mockingbirds and catbirds but spend much of their time upon the forest floor. Locally they are often called red mockingbirds or French mockingbirds. To the Cajuns of southern Louisiana they are known as *Moqueur des bois* or *Moqueur rouge*, the English equivalent of these names being "wood mocker" and "red mocker." The names are quite descriptive of the bird's habits and appearance. Looking much like an overgrown thrush, it is a bird of the deeper forests. Each of the three common members of the family Mimidae—the mockingbirds, catbirds, and thrashers—has its own personality and characteristics. The mockingbird prefers the more open woodlands and forest edges while the catbird inhabits the deeper woods. The thrasher is a woodland bird, especially favoring the wooded river bottoms. Nesting thrashers are quite pugnacious in defense of their young and a male will often chase a cat or a dog.

As I sit watching the thrasher scratching on the ground, I am impressed by its excellent camouflaging coloration, for it is difficult to spot this Moqueur on the ground among the brown leaves when viewed from above. A short distance away from the bird is an exposed patch of dust and it now flies over and spreads one wing and then the other as it ruffles its feathers in a dust bath, obviously enjoying the process. It seems strange that some birds, such as cardinals, indulge in water baths while others prefer to cleanse their feathers with dust. After a few minutes the thrasher tilts its head sidewise and looks up at me with one golden-irised eye, at the same time expressing its annoyance by a peculiar *tchai, tchai, tchai* note.

Then it darts away just above the ground and disappears into the forest. So far I have been successful in eluding all the ground-dwelling creatures of The Island but the keen eyes of the thrasher eventually detected my presence.

At this point I notice a pair of mockingbirds alight on the ground in a small sunlit opening some distance away to my left. One, probably the female, hops to the center of the open place and remains still, then the other alights opposite his mate and, after a moment, hops sidewise a few times. The actions of the male seemingly puts the female in a dancing mood so she follows suit and they both dance back and forth across the open space in the forest, always facing each other and about a foot apart. I am witnessing the mockingbird's dance ritual, one of the most interesting habits found among our wild birds. Whether or not these dances are entirely nuptial in nature is questionable since they may be performed at any time of the year and not just during the mating season. Usually, one or the other alights on the ground and takes the initiative; then, if the other is in the mood, they engage in their dance. Where the dance is performed seems unimportant; I have seen them dancing on flat rooftops and on paved highways.

After the mockingbirds have, seemingly, lost interest in each other and flown away, the forest floor reverts to its usual quiet. Occasional breezes disturb the trees, causing the patches of light and shadow to move slowly back and forth as I sit half-asleep on my perch and lose track of time. A chameleon crawls over a nearby limb, pauses for a moment or two, then moves slowly out of sight, searching as always for insect food. Gradually, a soft movement among the dry leaves beyond the stream brings me back to consciousness and, as I watch, a mother bobwhite quail with seven chicks emerges and hurries toward the water. The hen keeps a vigilant eye on the surroundings but the chicks run along on their short legs, stopping now and then to peck bugs from the short vegetation.

The little group congregates at the water's edge, alternately dipping their beaks and lifting their heads to allow the water to run down their throats. It is a pretty scene; always I am pleased by the actions of wild creatures quietly going about their business in natural surroundings. The hen tilts her head sidewise and looks directly up at me but I remain still and apparently she does not see me; her eyes are conditioned to other enemies, to hawks that, on occasion, dart out of the overhead foliage.

Having satisfied their thirst, the covey moves up the bank, some of the chicks milling aimlessly about, others squatting among the dead leaves, almost invisible because of their remarkable camouflaging coloration. Sometimes one individual or another lifts a foot and scratches rapidly at its beak or beneath a short wing. They are obviously enjoying the sun's warmth. Occasionally one chick rolls on its side, at the same time spreading out the opposite wing to absorb the heat. Eventually the little group moves off through the weeds, hurried along by the hen. For a time I can follow their progress by the soft rustlings of the dry leaves; then they are gone and the glade is left deserted.

With time on my hands, I now contemplate my leafy surroundings. The loud, discordant call of a pileated woodpecker echoes across the forest and is gone, leaving only the soft humming sounds of crickets to lull me into a half-somnolent state. Slowly my eyes wander away through the foliage, focusing here and there on leaves swaying in the sultry breezes. Then, for no logical reason, my attention is attracted to a certain twig on a nearby gum tree. Perhaps the twig has moved slightly in an untwig-like manner but the movement is so small that I am not sure that it has moved at all. Still, my eyes contiuue to focus on this particular twig.

Gradually the realization dawns on me that I am looking at an enormous walkingstick insect, its elongate body half-concealed among the star-shaped leaves. It is at least six inches in length and its legs resemble leaf stems. After a few moments the large insect moves again, crawling slowly and deliberately about as it seeks another leaf upon which to feed.

What I am seeing, I know, is a specimen of the giant walkingstick, the largest insect found beyond the realm of the true Tropics and

The giant walkingstick, Mega-phasma, is the largest insect found in North America. Measuring nearly six inches in length, it feeds on tree leaves. Its body form conceals it from enemies.

one that is not often seen. I suspect, however, that they are fairly common but due to their effective concealing form and dull coloration are seldom collected by entomologists.

As I watch, the specimen in the gum tree crawls slowly and deliberately upward among the leaves and I realize that it had only been by accident that my eyes had detected it at all.

There are walkingsticks of several kinds found in the trees on The Island but none as large as the giant walkingstick, known to science as *Megaphasma*, a name, by the way, of Greek origin, meaning "a large apparition or phantom." These insects are closely related to the praying mantises but while the latter are predators on other insects, the walkingsticks are all herbivorous, living among and feeding on tree leaves. When mature, the females drop their seed-like eggs to the forest floor where they remain until spring when the young hatch and crawl up into trees to live and feed.

The sun is now low on the horizon and I am reminded that evening is approaching. Ordinarily mosquitoes are not much of a problem on The Island but, as I perch in the live oak, I become conscious of their biting activities. Assuming that they are the usual salt-marsh mosquitoes that breed farther south in the coastal marshes and are carried inland by winds, I slap several on my arms. Then, since there is nothing else to engage my attention, I look closely at a specimen that is busily pumping blood out of my arm. Much to my surprise, it is a *Mansonia* mosquito, not only a vicious biter but one with most unusual habits while in the larval or wiggler stage. Like other mosquito larvae, those of *Mansonia* mosquitoes live in the water but, unlike most other kinds, do not obtain air by means of siphons or air tubes which are thrust up through the surface film. *Mansonia* larvae have evolved the unusual habit of thrusting their spine-like air siphons into the air-filled stems of submerged water plants, such as cattail and water hyacinth, making it unnecessary for them to rise to the water's surface.

The presence of these adult mosquitoes indicates that they are no

Left: *Here in this close-up, a giant walkingstick insect chews on the leaf of a sweet gum tree.* Right: *The eggs of the giant walkingstick resemble tiny hand grenades. They are dropped upon the forest floor where they remain until the following spring before hatching.*

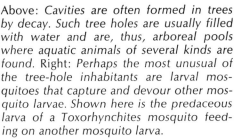

Above: *Cavities are often formed in trees by decay. Such tree holes are usually filled with water and are, thus, arboreal pools where aquatic animals of several kinds are found.* Right: *Perhaps the most unusual of the tree-hole inhabitants are larval mosquitoes that capture and devour other mosquito larvae. Shown here is the predaceous larva of a Toxorhynchites mosquito feeding on another mosquito larva.*

doubt breeding somewhere on The Island and I determine to locate the site in order to take pictures. Later, I investigated all the likely pools in the vicinity but was never able to locate their breeding habitat. However, in these investigations I did find out some other interesting things about The Island's mosquitoes. In the forest here, as in many other places, especially hardwood forests, deep cavities are frequently formed in trees by the dying or breaking-off of limbs. Often these cavities are a foot or more in depth and six or eight inches in diameter. They are created by localized decay and surrounded by living wood; thus, they collect rainwater, forming small arboreal pools, or microcosms, where a number of aquatic insects have taken up life. Several kinds of mosquito larvae are found in no other place. One of these is very large, as is the adult into which it transforms. The mature insect is brilliantly colored and has a long, downwardly bent proboscis, totally unfitted for sucking blood, and instead of blood, it feeds upon plant nectar.

Entomologists now classify these huge mosquitoes in the genus *Toxorhynchites* but they were formerly placed in the genus *Megarhinus*. Their larvae have a most unusual habit; they are predaceous on other mosquito larvae which also live in the tree holes. Thus, these mosquitoes are beneficial to man. In my investigations of tree-hole mosquitoes, I was fortunate in finding a number of these large larvae and in obtaining pictures of them in the act of feeding upon other mosquito larvae. By coincidence, some of these predaceous larvae were collected in a tree hole in the same live oak where I perched.

Leaving the oak slightly before dusk, I walk back across The Island. In some places, the forest floor is already in deep shadow and at several points I am forced to detour around swampy patches where the blooms of white spider lilies stand out in sharp contrast in the gathering gloom. My eyes are attracted by a slow movement among the leaves beside a cypress bole and, as I watch, a small snake crawls slowly into view. Walking over to investigate, I find it to be a hognose snake, often known, with good reason, as a spreading adder. A foot or so beyond sits a young toad, oblivious to the fact that it is being stalked by the snake.

The hognose snake *(Heterodon)* is of medium size and harmless, to humans, at least; it feeds upon toads and frogs which are grasped with the aid of a pair of fang-like teeth at the rear of the upper jaw. But it is this snake's other habits that are of special interest.

As I approach the cypress bole, the toad, alarmed at last, hops away while the snake raises its head and the front portion of its body several inches above the ground and flattens them, giving it somewhat the aspect of a deadly cobra. This pose is supposed to scare me away but, since it does not, the snake then gives vent to a loud hiss. When even this does not frighten me away, the amusing snake then begins the next part of its act; it throws its body into violent contortions, writhing about as if in the throes of death. This continues for half a minute, then it flips over on its back and suddenly appears to be dead. This, I know, is merely a part of its performance since, presumably, a dead snake is of no interest to any

Left: *The hognose snake or spreading adder, when alarmed, flattens its head and neck, giving it the appearance of a cobra. But it is harmless.* Right: *When disturbed, a spreading adder turns over on its back and "plays possum," a ruse that probably protects it from enemies.*

enemy except, perhaps, a buzzard.

Picking up a stick, I flip the "dead" snake over on its belly, with the result that it immediately turns over on its back again. This is the flaw in its act; a spreading adder apparently "thinks" that a dead snake must be on its back; when playing 'possum, it always turns upside-down. When disturbed, it always follows this same routine and, from the standpoint of natural selection, its act apparently aids in survival. Its generic name, by the way, is "*contortrix*" in reference to its habit of contorting its body when it pretends to "die."

Now that the spreading adder is in the final stage of its show and lies as if dead on the ground, I walk away some distance and sit down on a log. For perhaps five minutes it remains "dead," then slowly "comes to life" and crawls away, none the worse for its experience except for the fact that its dinner has escaped.

I, too, move away through the gathering gloom, now in a pensive mood. Today I have been a privileged observer of some of the ways in which The Island's inhabitants achieve survival in a world where keen competition is the normal way of life. Through my mind there runs a familiar quotation from William Cullen Bryant's "Thanatopsis:"

> To him who in the love of Nature holds
> Communion with her visible forms, she speaks
> A various language . . .

Chapter 5

ALONG THE TRAIL TO NOWHERE

ALONG THE NORTH SIDE of The Island meanders a trail that, in the usual sense, leads to nowhere in particular. It begins near a dense growth of cane or bamboo near the river and curves away through the pines, at one point approaching the island's northern shore. It then turns abruptly inland and crosses a marshy area, beyond which it terminates as suddenly and as mysteriously as it began. Whether man-made or not I do not know; perhaps it merely resulted from a chance growth of trees and bushes and was not really intended as a path at all. Perhaps, too, it was created by the feet of wild animals since it forms a natural passageway across that portion of The Island. In support of this idea, I have often noticed the footprints of 'coons, 'possums, and feral hogs in its muddy portions. I have the feeling that at night, when all is quiet, this pathway is traversed by the dark mysterious forms of wild creatures going about their nocturnal affairs. Unfortunately I have never explored this portion of The Island at night and so do not really know what animals pass this way after the sun drops down beyond the western savannah. Someday I will set up a camera and flash rig beside this trail, so arranged that any passing creature will take its own picture. This would solve the mystery once and for all.

The forest along the way is composed of vegetation in great variety, varying from small bushes to live oaks whose limbs stretch out like great arms over the floor of the forest. The oaks are scat-

73

Left: *The longleaf pine has the longest needles of any pine, often measuring eighteen inches in length. This is a seedling.* Right: *The bald cypress sheds its leaves in autumn, hence its name. As seen here, fresh foliage is produced each spring.*

tered here and there some distance apart and interspersed among them are pines of two varieties. The longleaf pines *(Pinus palustris)* rise nearly a hundred feet into the air and bear great cones as long as ten inches; their needles are the longest of any pine, often measuring a foot and a half in length. Then, at one point along the trail, there are slash pines *(Pinus caribaea)*, stately trees growing straight as rods and bearing at their tops a few spreading limbs held disdainfully, it would seem, above the lesser trees. These two kinds of pines are the source of turpentine and resin, which are bled from them in various places along this coastal zone.

While the pines grow tall and straight, the live oaks are short and stubby, making up in spread for their lack of height. Majestic and imposing, their enormous limbs are always draped with Spanish moss and support growths of epiphytic ferns along their upper surfaces. Beneath them the island's sandy soil is shaded from the sun and remains moist, an ideal habitat for centipedes and snails. Live oaks survive to great age and impart to the places where they grow a sense of quiet dignity and permanence. They, like magnolias, thrive in the soft southern breezes and humid air. On The Island, I have rested in their shade during hot afternoons and perched on their horizontal limbs to watch the life of the forest.

Second only to the live oaks in beauty—a matter of personal opinion—is the magnolia, definitely a tree of the Deep South. On The Island there are several superb specimens of great size, but scattered in the shade of other forest trees, their numerous seedlings struggle for light and space. The large oval leaves of the magnolias glisten in the sun like polished metal and, in early summer, their great snow-white blooms unfold, wafting away their heavy scent through the night to attract the beetles upon which they depend for pollination. Later, from the seed burs, emerge scarlet seeds that, in time, fall to the ground or are carried away by birds. This tree has an ancient lineage; together with the buttercups, it evolved long ago when the earth was young. Like the live oak, it is a symbol of the South and of a graceful way of life.

On several occasions I have climbed into the upper reaches of a large magnolia where, far above the earth, the great branches snaked away from the trunk. Here, cut off from the surrounding forest by the mass of foliage, I found myself at the center of a leafy world where even the light was tinged with emerald green and where the only movement was that of small lizards darting about on the branches in their eternal search for insect food. Always reluctant, I climbed down to rejoin the normal world from which I had been isolated for a time within the living canopy of a tree.

Also along the trail, in various other damp situations, grow the ubiquitous bald cypress trees, rising out of the island's muck like vertical columns. Flanking one portion of the trail, they line the way, their swollen buttresses almost obscuring the more distant vistas. In autumn their feathery foliage turns reddish brown, then falls away, leaving bare branches against the sky. It is for this reason that they are called "bald" cypresses. They are interspersed with tupelo gums, large trees with somewhat similar habits of growth but which almost always grow with their bases in the water. Often, at first glance, while walking along the trail, I have mistakenly called a tupelo a cypress. It is only by looking upward at the foliage that one can be sure of the identification, since the tupelo bears leaves, not needle-like foliage as do the cypresses. The cypresses belong to the great class of coniferous trees while the tupelos are classified among the broad-leaved trees and are rather closely related to the dogwood and the black gum. Known to science as *Nyssa aquatica*, the tupelo's name is appropriate since it means "a post that grows in the water." Strangely, most of this tree's relatives now grow only in Malaysia, Mongolia, and the Himalayas.

Scattered here and there along the trail grow slender trees with dark, shiny leaves that, when crushed between the fingers, are very fragrant. Known as sweet bay or swamp bay, these trees are closely related to the large magnolia; in fact, they are true magnolias but of a different species. While walking along, I often pick off bay leaves and crush them for their pleasing, pungent smell. In autumn the wet, black muck of the swampy areas is strewn with their scarlet seeds, adding touches of bright color to the dark forest floor.

Probably the most common tree along the trail, as well as on other parts of The Island, is the hop hornbeam or ironwood *(Ostrya)*,

Often, the roots of trees rise in arching curves above the earth.

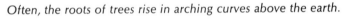

The flower clusters of titi brighten The Island's forest. Bees of many kinds gather their nectar.

a tree of the deep forests. Closely related to the birch, this tree has gray or brownish bark, usually mottled in attractive patterns by lichens. In early summer it produces cone-like clusters of leafy appendages within which the seeds are contained. Since this cone resembles the fruit of the hop, the tree is known as the hop hornbeam, but due to the hardness of its wood it is also called ironwood. Because of its small, scattered leaves, the sunlight falling from above is broken into patches of light and shadow on the forest floor and flashes of sunlight splash upon the varicolored trunk and limbs.

It would be impossible to cover within the scope of this book all the characteristic trees along the trail, but one other tree I must mention. This is the titi, sometimes also known as ironwood. Today, as I walk along the trail I see only the small specimens with their crooked trunks and bright green leaves. In March, however, the titis deck themselves out in racemes of small, white, nodding blooms which are most fragrant and which bees find attractive for the sweet nectar they contain. When the blooms are gone their places are taken by small seed pods resembling those of buckwheat.

Today, as on so many other hot summer days, I walk along the path through the varied growth of trees, pausing now and then to investigate the plant and animal life found there. Numerous fallen and decaying tree trunks offer interesting possibilities so I roll some

Strange ribbon worms live on the moist earth along the trail or on low vegetation.

of them over, always hoping to find unusual inhabitants hidden beneath. Such decaying trunks, I have found, are ideal sites to look for specimens. While alive, a tree is host to many animals as well as various forms of plant life, including lichens, mosses, and ferns, but after its death it becomes the abode of even more living things. As a tree grows, it absorbs minerals from the soil throughout its long life, but nature has a way of balancing her books. In time, the tree dies and its minerals return to the soil out of which they came. They are borrowed and must be repaid, following an ancient and irrefutable law.

This prostrate trunk beside the path was once a towering forest tree; it held its leaves up to the sunlight to absorb its energy. Through the years of its life it produced seeds for the continuation of its species and, each spring, furnished sites for nesting birds. Lichens and mosses found anchorage on its spreading limbs, and insects of infinite variety fed upon its leaves. But inevitably its time ran out and its vital processes ceased to function; death overtook the tree and it crashed, at last, to the earth out of which it came. Its decaying trunk is now almost completely covered by a soft carpet of green moss plants. Once, many millions of years ago, the ancestors of these mosses were gigantic in size, as large as the largest trees of this island forest. But that was long ago and now their small descendants merely creep over the remains of forest giants that were evolved long after the mosses had their heyday. Thus does time move on and make its changes; the great become the small and

Tiny mosses grow upon the spreading live oak limbs. Millions of years ago their ancestors grew as large as trees but now, reduced in size, they exist on rotting wood and on the limbs of trees.

the small become the **great**.

Soon after this immense tree was felled, perhaps by a hurricane, microscopic moss spores drifted onto its surface and germinated in the moisture. From these spores grew thread-like protonemas which spread over the soft wood, in time producing the numerous small moss plants, each with its green leafy stem. They now grow crowded closely together like the pile of a carpet and will, eventually, give rise to more spores, continuing the ancient chain of moss life reaching out of the past and into the future.

I roll back the green carpet, exposing the rotting wood beneath. Alarmed by the sudden light are many small living things; a two-inch centipede scurries into a crevice and disappears, a snail with-

Mosses and liverworts creep over the moist surfaces of rotten logs along the trail. Shown here are liverworts. The holes, lower left, were made by wood-boring beetles.

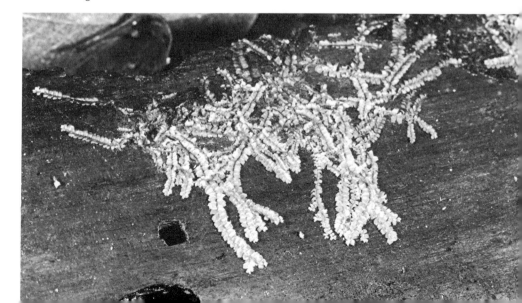

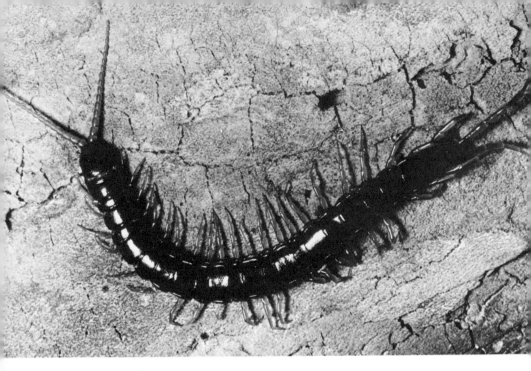

Above: *Centipedes are common beneath the bark of decaying logs. They run rapidly and disappear quickly into crevices. Left: Shown close-up are a centipede's poison fangs (see arrow). The fangs are used mostly for capturing prey, and the bite of these centipedes is not dangerous.*

draws into its coiled fortress, while a millipede as large as a pencil curls up and "plays 'possum." Here and there over the moist surface spread the white mycelia of creeping molds. Using my machete, which I always carry while exploring the forest, I chop into the soft, yielding wood, splitting it apart. Now I reveal a deeper realm, the habitat of many other forms of life. An endless maze of small passages extends through the decomposing wood and in and out of these run dozens of white termites. The workers, each an eighth of an inch in length, are completely white, but now and then I see members of the soldier caste with their dark, elongate heads and large jaws. Their duty is probably that of defending the colony against enemies. I notice that these soldier termites often pause and strike their heads rapidly against the wood and, when I listen closely, I can hear the small tapping sounds they make. Some authorities believe these sounds to be rallying calls or signals, given to alert the colony of danger or to call other soldiers. Even though they are blind, termites are repelled by light, so within a minute or so they all disappear into their tunnels and are gone.

Termites are of two types; there are dry-wood termites and subterranean termites. Those I exposed were of the latter type. Dry-wood termites do not require moist places for their nests. Subterranean termites, on the other hand, are moisture-loving and always establish their nests in damp places such as the ground or decaying wood. These are the ones chiefly responsible for damage to human habitations. While they usually establish their colonies in the ground, they often construct covered tunnels above ground through

A millipede as large as a pencil crawls slowly across a sandy area of the forest floor.

Termites in endless numbers live within the dead wood of fallen trees. Completely blind, they feed upon the woody tissues.

which they travel to sources of woody food. Sometimes these tunnels extend up over the brick foundations of houses. Here on The Island I found such tunnels running up the sides of a tree, a most unusual occurrence.

Termites are among the most remarkable of all insects; unable to digest the wood through which they tunnel, they have adopted guest-animals (Protozoa) which live within their intestines and digest the wood fibers for them. Without these guests the termites would be unable to exist. Termites are social insects; that is, they live together in populous colonies having a queen that lays the eggs for the production of the labor force of blind workers, as well as soldiers, kings, and queens. Very ancient, they were evolved long before other social insects such as hornets and bees.

Deeper in the log, I find a number of relatively large passages filled with macerated wood fibers. These, I know, are the living quarters of passalid beetles and their grub-like young. Sometimes called betsy bugs, these insects are nearly two inches long, jet black in color, and upon the tops of their thoraxes have forwardly directed horns or hooks. Because of this they are also known as horned passalus beetles. The most unusual feature of these wood-inhabiting insects is the fact that of all the members of the beetle tribe, as far as I know, they are the only ones which have developed semi-social habits. The adults and their clumsy grubs live in small colonies deep in decaying logs. The hind legs of the larvae are reduced to stubby, finger-like organs fitted only to rasp upon a roughened area of the body to produce stridulations or squeaking sounds. Evidently this is a primitive form of communication, helping, perhaps, to keep the colony together or to warn each other of danger. On the other hand, when I break open their tunnels there is no effort at defense; indeed, these beetles' only defense is escape. Picking one adult up in my fingers I find that it, too, makes a squeaking sound. I examine it carefully under a hand lens and find it to be heavily infested with tiny mites or ticks. These parasites scurry about over the beetle's armor-like surface like fleas on a rat. Seemingly even betsy bugs have their troubles!

Chopping on into the log I soon expose a globular mass of dried grass and, when this is explored with my fingers, find four young animals which at first appear to be mice. However, when I attempt to lift the nest and its contents out for further examination I discover the mother hiding in a deeper recess of the wood. Somewhat astonished, I see that she is a shrew, not a mouse at all. She is hardly over two inches long—just a little larger than the betsy bugs—and I can see no evidence of eyes.

Carefully I remove the shrew nest and its contents and place it in a plastic bag, then take steps to capture the mother, who remains motionless in the cavity, her long nose twitching nervously. I am somewhat fearful of catching her in my bare hands. Shrews not only have needle-sharp teeth, but the saliva of some kinds contains a poisonous venom. However, I take a chance and am successful in seizing her with my fingers just behind the head. When placed in the bag she quickly disappears into the nest to join her young. Of all the rotten logs I have rolled over and dug into during my many forays in the woods, this is the only time I have ever found a nest of one of these little animals.

Later, aboard the houseboat, I removed the nest containing the mother shrew and her young from the plastic bag and made photographs. The mother was very shy and I had considerable difficulty in getting her to pose. Back in my studio, I kept this interesting lit-

A mother shrew and her blind, naked young were discovered in a rotten log. Subsisting on insects and mice, they have voracious appetites; a shrew has been known to eat twice its weight within a few hours.

tle family in a cage for several months, feeding the mother, and later, her young on insects. She never became tame in any sense of the word; shrews are secretive, shy, and mysterious in their habits. By contrast, white-footed mice, who also nest in rotten logs, become quite tame when kept for some time in captivity.

While shrews are rather mouse-like and are sometimes called "long-nosed mice," they belong to an entirely different animal group—the Insectivora, or insect-eaters. Mice, on the other hand, belong to the Rodentia or gnawing animals, among which are also rats, muskrats, beavers, and similar animals. Shrews are closely related to the moles and, like them, spend most of their time in passages beneath the ground searching for living insects or other game. At night, however, they run about on the surface, and some kinds have aquatic habits. Once, many years ago in a Montana marsh, I saw a water shrew while I sat quietly waiting for a red-winged blackbird to return to her nest so that I could take her photograph. The tiny mammal came out of the dense growth of marsh plants and entered a shallow pool of clear water where it walked about on the bottom just as though no water were present. It remained submerged for at least a minute, apparently searching for aquatic insects, then emerged and disappeared into the vegetation.

On the western ranch where I grew up, domestic cats often captured shrews and brought them to the house, but they never ate them. Apparently they have a disagreeable, musky taste and so are probably unappetizing to most predators. To biologists, however, shrews are of special interest because, of all the world's carnivorous animals, they are probably the most voracious. A shrew has an enormous appetite and must consume its weight in flesh every few hours to remain alive. While many kinds live upon insects, others regularly attack and kill mice several times their own size. The well-known naturalist C. Hart Merriam once placed three shrews in a glass container for observation. They immediately commenced fighting and within a few minutes one was killed and devoured by the other two. A couple of hours later, one of the remaining shrews killed and ate the other. Thus, in effect, one of these tiny beasts had killed and eaten two individuals of its own kind, each as large as itself!

Because of their elusive habits, shrews have often been regarded with superstition. During the Middle Ages, it was believed that the shrew's bite was poisonous but authorities later scoffed at this idea. Recently, however, it was found that the bites of some shrews are actually quite poisonous; their saliva contains a toxin rather similar to that of snake venom. The saliva from a short-tailed shrew, for instance, contains sufficient poison to kill a hundred mice! In addition to their other unusual characteristics, some shrews are able to run rapidly over the surfaces of woodland pools, a feat made possible by bristles on their feet.

I rolled over several other logs in various stages of decay and hacked into them, but nothing very exciting was revealed. Finally, in a last attempt, I poked the blade of my machete into a decomposing heap of rotten wood that was little more than brown organic matter. At first nothing worth collecting was seen. Then I noticed an elongated insect larva which appeared to be that of a click beetle. Such larva, which are quite common, eventually transform into two-inch beetles known as eyed elaters because of two large eye-spots on the top of the prothorax. These eyespots are luminous in similar beetles found in certain tropical areas, but the eyespots of the North American variety emit no light.

I picked the larva up in my fingers and found, to my delight, that it was not a larval eyed elater at all but a *Phengodes*. This was a rare find so I carefully placed her in a vial. In my many years of collecting specimens, this was the second time I had seen one. Now you may wonder why I just spoke of this larval beetle as *her* since the sex of larval insects is usually impossible to determine. This is an interesting little story in itself. The male *Phengodes* is beetle-like and develops from a larva somewhat smaller than the one I just found. As an adult, it has large, feathery antennae. On the other hand, the female larva is much larger and this is the remarkable part of the story; she never transforms into the adult beetle stage, but mates and lays eggs while still a larva! Biologists have a name for this sort of thing; it is called *paedogenesis*, the bearing of young by immature animals. This in itself is unique, but these strange females have yet another unusual characteristic; they have a series of light-emitting organs along the sides of their bodies which, in darkness, glow with a greenish luminescence.

I was fairly certain that I had found a *Phengodes* female, but it was not until I had had a chance to observe the specimen aboard the houseboat at night that I knew for sure. In a glass container she crawled slowly about, her photogenic organs glowing with an eerie greenish light. Having captured such an unusual specimen, I decided to try an experiment; I set up a camera in the dark and waited until the *Phengodes* became quiet. Then, by the light of a flashlight, I focused the camera and made a series of thirty-second exposures with the lens wide open and no artificial illumination. Later, when the film was developed, I was gratified to find that the insect's image had been faithfully recorded by the glow of its own lights!

The Trail That Leads to Nowhere passes beside a small titi tree

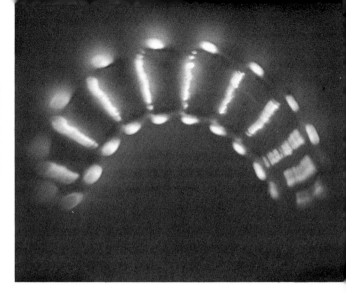

One of the most remarkable of all the creatures living within rotten logs is Phengodes, *the larval form of a beetle that glows with self-produced light. This picture was made by light from the insect.*

and continues its meandering way through the forest. At some points the surrounding vegetation is dense and impenetrable, consisting of a tangle of smilax or greenbrier vines with vicious, recurved spines that can tear the clothing or flesh. Their tough stems twine upward on supporting trees and shrubs and often make travel through the forest very difficult. These and other lianas are a characteristic of the semitropical forests of this area; unable to "stand on their own feet," they stretch upward toward the sunlight, taking advantage of the trunks of trees.

Here and there along the trail stand pawpaw trees, sometimes called false bananas, with their small, dark purple blooms. In autumn, the leaves, too, turn purple and the strange, bi-lobed fruit matures. It tastes like banana; hence, the second name. I pause here along the trail to examine a pawpaw tree more closely, trying to see some similarity to its relatives which I have known in tropical lands, the custard-apple, sweet sop, and sour sop. All these trees are classified as Annonaceae, a tree family whose members live mostly in the Tropics. There are more than five hundred kinds found within the tropical zone, but only a few have extended their ranges northward into our area. Around the earth's bulging waist there stretches a special world of plant life, teeming in almost infinite variety and form, but only in isolated instances have these plants and trees escaped from the hot lands to establish themselves within our borders.

While examining the pawpaw trees, I am surprised to see an unusual vine with heart-shaped leaves climbing up its trunk. Strangest of all, suspended from this vine are a number of globular growths resembling potatoes. Here, I realize, is an odd coincidence; the pawpaw long ago established itself in our area while this unusual vine is an air potato, indigenous to the tropical home of the pawpaw's relatives. How is it that I find them growing together here on an island along the Gulf of Mexico? The pawpaw, of course, is a naturalized American, so to speak, but the air potato probably grew here accidentally since they are often grown in this coastal area for their attractive foliage. The aerial tubers, if planted, will produce the characteristic vines. These climbing yams are of many kinds. I recall the strange spiny yam of the South Pacific Islands which produces a mass of thorns on the surface of the ground to protect its underground tubers. The generic name of the air potato is *Dioscorea*, in honor of Pedanius Dioscorides, an early Greek physician and herbalist who traveled widely as a surgeon with the Roman army and wrote a treatise on *materia medica* which remained a standard reference for many centuries.

Along the trail are found land turtles of two kinds, the box turtles and the gopher turtles. Little box turtles, *Terrapene*, are common and I have often seen them ambling about in their clumsy fashion. In autumn they congregate beneath the pawpaw trees, feeding upon the fallen fruit. Farther north, on the mainland, they

At some points on the trail the ground is very wet, forcing the roots of trees to grow on the surface in tangled masses in the semitropical environment.

The air potato (Dioscorea), a native of the Tropics, is a type of yam found on The Island. A climbing vine, it produces aerial tubers or "potatoes."

feed on wild plums but their food list includes almost any succulent plant or fruit. This morning I encountered a box turtle near the pawpaw thicket. It gave me one look, then withdrew its head and legs into its shell and closed up so tightly that there was no chink in its armor. Its shell or carapace is dome-like and the floor of its shell or plastron has two doors, fore and aft, both hinged to a central portion. When alarmed, a box turtle withdraws all four legs and head into its box-like fortress and closes its doors so tightly that usually not even a knife blade can be inserted. It sometimes happens, though, that well-fed box turtles are unable to withdraw their appendages completely since the shell will hold only so much turtle. In such a case it is amusing to watch the creature attempt to close its doors with its head and feet still protruding. The muscles of a box turtle's hinged openings are very powerful and if a person's fingers should accidentally get between door and shell before it is completely closed, they may be severely pinched. As can be imagined, a box turtle is quite invulnerable once its trap doors are closed, and dogs often bite at them but are apparently never successful in doing much damage to the amusing creatures.

In spring, box turtles excavate holes in the damp earth of The Island and, turning about, lay their white, leathery eggs. After covering up the nest with their hind legs, they walk away with never a backward look, leaving the eggs to the warmth of the southern sun for incubation. Like many other animals, box turtles have very decided home preferences and are able to find their way back when released at a considerable distance. Apparently they orient themselves by the sun and often go astray on cloudy days.

While box turtles are quite common in the pine forest of The Island and are often seen, I never found evidence of gopher turtles or tortoises until recently. Beyond the growth of pawpaws lies a sandy stretch near an ancient magnolia tree, now in full bloom. Here and there are mounds of sand, and when I investigate I find

Box turtles live on dry land, subsisting on fallen fruit and succulent vegetation. They have strong homing instincts and can find their way back to their home territory by sun navigation. When alarmed, a box turtle withdraws its head, legs, and tail into its shell and closes it tightly.

The gopher tortoise (Gopherus polyphemus) lives in a long burrow which it excavates in the sandy soil. A number of other animals take up residence in these burrows, including certain beetles, frogs, and snakes.

the openings to several tunnels. The entrances to these tunnels or burrows are about eight inches across and six inches high and the only creatures I can think of that might excavate such burrows are gopher turtles, more properly called tortoises. I have never really become accustomed to calling these creatures gophers, since in the West we always spoke of ground squirrels as gophers. Regional names are often quite confusing.

The true tortoises usually inhabit the world's more desertlike regions such as those of Africa, the Malagasy Republic, and certain Pacific Islands. Giant tortoises are common on the Galápagos Islands and often weigh more than three hundred pounds. By contrast, our gopher tortoise is a midget, rarely measuring over a foot long or weighing over ten pounds. It is our only true tortoise and is seldom seen because of its nocturnal and subterranean habits.

Returning to the houseboat, I obtained a spade with which to dig away the earth, following the burrow which I suspected to have been made by a gopher turtle. Fortunately the ground was sandy so the work progressed rapidly except when tree roots were en-

countered. For several feet the tunnel followed along only a foot
below the surface; then it angled deeper. I squatted down and
peered into the dark opening but could see nothing, so I continued
digging, a task which was now becoming quite arduous.

In this fashion I exposed another yard or so of the burrow, then
examined it again. I could still see no evidence of the gopher turtle,
but I did see several small scarab beetles about a quarter of an inch
long crawling about on the level floor. Recalling that there are
insects of several different kinds which live in gopher burrows and
are found nowhere else, I captured some of the specimens and
placed them in a vial for future identification.

It is a strange fact that when almost any animal adopts the habit
of living in a permanent abode, it is apt to be joined by free-loaders
who take advantage of its hospitality. In the case of the gopher tortoise, these "star boarders" range all the way from the gopher frog
to numerous insects, all of which have found safe homes in the
burrows. Among the varied assemblage of insect guests are these
scarab beetles, rove beetles, and hister beetles, as well as the larva of
a moth and a wingless cricket. Within the cave-like burrows, the insects apparently feed as scavangers and are comparatively safe from
birds and most other enemies. Ross Allen of Silver Springs, Florida,
once excavated a gopher turtle burrow and found, in addition to
the rightful owner, an opossum, a rabbit, a gopher frog, and a five-
foot diamondback rattlesnake!

I had about decided that my excavation of the gopher tunnel was
turning out to be a bigger task than I had anticipated when I heard
a thumping sound from deep within the burrow. With renewed
enthusiasm I dug on and was soon rewarded by the sight of the
inhabitant—a gopher tortoise. Reaching into the tunnel, I grasped
one stubby foreleg and tried to pull it out but found that it had
apparently wedged itself so tightly in the narrow passage that I was
forced to dig again. Eventually I dug around the specimen and
hauled the struggling creature out. It was an adult, about eight
inches across and slate-black in color. Its feet were elephant-like
and bore blunt claws instead of toes, an ideal arrangement for dig-

ging. Its dome-like carapace was set with diamond-shaped plates in which the yearly growth rings or zones could clearly be discerned. When released on the ground the gopher waddled rapidly off, but I retrieved it easily and placed it in a cloth bag, brought along for the purpose.

Later, back at my home, I kept this unusual tortoise in a greenhouse, feeding it on lettuce and other vegetables. It was a docile and interesting pet and, while never actually tame, it did become used to humans and would accept food from my fingers.

Doing some library research on land tortoises of the United States, I found that there are three different kinds, all belonging to the genus *Gopherus*. The one I dug out on The Island was *Gopherus polyphemus*, the species which ranges from the Carolinas to Louisiana. In Texas and northeastern Mexico there is another species, *Gopherus berlandieri*, known as the Texas tortoise. In addition to these, there is a third species, *Gopherus agassizi*, found in the desert areas of the southwestern United States and known as the desert tortoise. However, all three kinds are quite similar in appearance and habits and their differences may be considered minor except, perhaps, to a professional herpetologist.

The trail, beyond the gopher turtle den, winds on through the pines and I had walked but a short distance when something at my feet suddenly darted away at amazing speed; it appeared to be a snake, but no snake can travel that fast. Some distance away the creature, whatever it was, disappeared into a patch of tall grass. Walking over, I peered down into the tangled vegetation but, at first, could see nothing. As my eyes became adjusted to the light, I saw the slender form of a glass "snake." It made no move so I grabbed at it with my hand. I missed its body, but my fingers did come in contact with its tail and the next instant I found only a three-inch piece of the tail between my fingers; the rest of the "snake" was gone. I dropped the severed tail on the ground where it thrashed about for several seconds, shedding a few drops of blood.

My experience with this glass "snake" *(Ophisaurus)* is typical of what usually takes place when an enemy attempts to capture

The glass "snake" is actually a legless lizard or skink. When captured by an enemy, it severs its tail and escapes; in the meantime, the tail thrashes about in the grass, probably attracting the enemy's attention. Later, the glass "snake" grows a new tail.

one; it automatically severs its tail by the contraction of special muscles. In the meantime, the "snake" darts away, eventually, to grow a new tail. Sometimes, it happens that the tail is not completely severed. When this occurs, the regenerative processes are stimulated to begin the production of a new tail which grows out of the partial break. As a result, the "snake" becomes the owner of *two* tails! When someone finds one of these freaks he usually thinks he has made scientific history by discovering a forked-tailed snake.

In truth, the glass "snake" is not really a snake at all but a lizard that, through the processes of evolution, has lost its legs. It has all the other characteristics of the skink-like lizards, including the habit of severing its tail when captured. When an enemy attempts to seize one of these "snakes" the severed end thrashes about vigorously in the grass, attracting attention away from the main part of the creature, which is thus enabled to escape.

It was near this point along the trail that I made a very interesting discovery, one that has apparently been reported by no one else. Almost always, on my island excursions, I see numerous lubber grasshoppers (*Brachystola*). They are black, heavy-bodied, and clumsy and walk about over the ground, giving every appearance of being thoughtful and wise. In truth, they are very "stupid" insects whose only defense apparently lies in hopping rapidly away; their wings are short and flight is impossible.

It is known, of course, that lubber grasshoppers lay their egg masses in the earth during late autumn and that the young emerge the following spring. One autumn I was walking along the trail and noticed, a few feet away, an area of exposed sand about ten feet in diameter. It was white, as usual, and raised somewhat above the level of the surrounding forest. Such patches of exposed sand are not uncommon on The Island but what causes them I do not know. Anyway, on this particular occasion my attention was attracted by a number of lubber grasshoppers congregated on the sand. This

On this sandy area in the island forest, lubber grasshoppers congregate in autumn to mate, lay eggs, and die. Note the female, far left, with her abdomen buried in the sand as she lays eggs. Dead grasshoppers are seen in the foreground.

was a little unusual since they are not normally gregarious except when young. Looking more closely I found several pairs in the process of mating and four or five females with their abdomens inserted deeply in the soil in the act of laying eggs. Scattered around the margin of the sandy patch I was astonished to notice dozens of dead grasshoppers, both males and females. Here was some food for thought and I at last decided that apparently the lubber grasshoppers of The Island had congregated at this site to mate, lay eggs, and die. I searched the surrounding forest but found only an occasional lubber grasshopper, though I did find three other mating sites. Later, I explored other islands along the river and was pleased to discover a number of other such places.

As I watched these great, clumsy grasshoppers mating, laying eggs, and dying on isolated spots in the forest I was reminded of the fabled graveyards of the elephants—the areas where old, enfeebled elephants retire to die. There are, of course, no such places but such was once the popular belief. Perhaps there is no similarity between elephant graveyards and lubber grasshopper breeding sites, yet the locations to which these grasshoppers retire when ready to

Close-up of a lubber grasshopper with her abdomen buried in the sand in the act of egg-laying. Lubber grasshoppers are large and heavy-bodied. Their wings are short and of no use in flight.

While laying eggs, a female lubber grasshopper is not easily disturbed. This one sat quietly while her abdomen was exposed. The eggs are ejected in a mass of foamy material that slowly hardens.

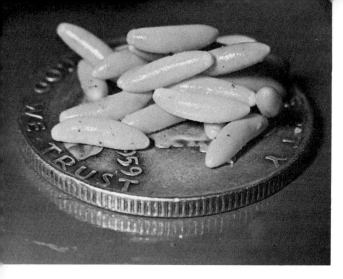

This close-up shows a cluster of lubber grasshopper eggs on a fifty-cent piece. When the young hatch in the spring, they remain together in a small group.

mate are also their graveyards. In Nature's economy, once having mated and laid their eggs they have no further function in life to fulfill, and so they die.

As an illustration of the bovine-like character of these amusing grasshoppers, I tried a little experiment. I located a female with her abdomen deeply buried in the soil in the act of egg-laying and excavated away the sandy soil, leaving the tip of her abdomen exposed. As far as I could tell she remained totally unconscious of my presence and, every minute or so, I could see another egg emerge from her ducts. Normally these would eventually form an underground cluster, but there she sat, her abdomen completely exposed while egg after egg was ejected. Seemingly, once her instincts had been triggered to lay eggs, she had no choice but to continue. Even when I set up camera and electronic flash to record the consummation of her maternal act, she calmly continued to lay eggs. Having finished recording this little woodland drama on film, I walked away with a feeling that I had been a privileged observer at a strange ritual, one that always ended in death. I had discovered the birthplace and graveyard of the grasshoppers.

Chapter 6

QUIET DAYS

WALKING IS THE TIME to think; it is also the time to see. I suppose that when walking the mind is freed from other things and more able to digest what the senses transmit to it. My best ideas arise while shaving and while walking, but I much prefer the latter. Early morning walks on The Island are my favorites and consist of slow meanderings and pauses; I stop to examine an insect on a leaf, detour for a closer look at a mushroom, or am lured from the path to pull the bark from a stump to see what hides beneath it. In a sense, my walks are not walks at all but small exploratory expeditions. I see the gross anatomy of the island forest, its trees and climbing vines, but I am also aware of the infinite variety of living things they harbor and, through long observation, have learned how to interpret many of the things I see.

This morning as I stroll across The Island I notice a large wasp coursing back and forth just above the ground near a clump of palmettos. Its body is marked with golden cross-bars and it flies with purposeful intent. Because of its size and coloration it is easily identified as *Bembix carolina*, a common wasp of the South. Knowing somewhat of its habits, I am sure that this one is a female searching for horseflies, which will be stung and stored in an underground burrow as food for her future young. Somewhere in the vicinity, no doubt, she has already excavated a burrow in the sand, needing only a stock of paralyzed horseflies and her egg to complete the act of nest-building. Nearby, crawling over the sand, is a wingless mutilid wasp, or velvet "ant," nearly half an inch in length and covered with orange-red hair. I know that if I pick this insect up in my fingers I will receive a painful sting. The velvet ant appears to be crawling aimlessly across the sand but, familiar with the ways of such insects, I know that this one is a female searching for the underground nest of a wasp, such as that of *Bembix*, in which to lay an egg that her larva may live as a parasite on the wasp larva. The latter larva will eventually die as a result. Some distance away, a large hornet-like wasp alights on the ground. It is black with white bars. Looking closely, I notice that it is regurgitating water onto the hard earth. When a spot as large as a dime has been moistened, the wasp gathers up a pellet of the mud and flies away through the forest. This is *Monobia quadridens*, a lazy wasp that uses an abandoned carpenter bee tunnel in solid wood as a nesting site. No doubt she has already provisioned it with paralyzed caterpillars and will use the pellet of mud to seal the outside entrance, her final act in nesting.

Each wild inhabitant is engaged on a definite errand; it has some instinctive purpose to fulfill. If I were to stand at the window of a tall building and look down upon the people hurrying along the busy street it might appear that these "ants" were walking about with no special intent; yet, I would know that each one was going to a definite place to engage in a definite business. It is more or less the same with the wild creatures of the forest.

Even though I explore the Island again and again at various seasons I am almost certain to find something new each time. This is a rather astonishing fact and proves that one need not cover a large area to find things of interest. In winter, the woods are far different from the way they looked in the summer; even the birds are different. Many of the summer residents have flown southward across the Gulf, perhaps to Yucatán. Mostly these are the insect-eaters that must follow the sun to lands of continuous summer. In winter the island forest is inhabited by birds that have nested in more northern regions, some as far away as Canada. Here on The Island they remain during the cooler months, foraging for seeds.

Red bay (Persea), *growing along The Island's margins, produces blue-black fruit.*

The robins search for worms in the damp soil but they sing no songs and, when seeing them, I am assailed by a feeling of nostalgia. In the Northwest, where I was reared, the voices of robins were the harbingers of spring and I thrilled to the sound, knowing that the long northern winter was over at last. Sometimes, of course, these first robins were betrayed by the weather and late snows fell upon the nesting birds, often covering the females an inch in depth as they sat on their nests. Yet, this was merely a calculated risk in the lives of the robins and their sky-blue eggs hatched on schedule. In that climate, the plants, too, were remarkably adapted to the seasons. Glacier lilies pushed up through the snow, stimulated by the lengthening days and the sun that was warming the soil.

Those who dwell in southern climates, especially in the Tropics, have little conception of what the coming of spring really means. To them the weather merely becomes drier or warmer, as the case may be, but there is never the thrill of hearing the song of the first robin or of seeing the bright blooms of early spring flowers pushing out of the ground. I once attempted to tell a South Sea native what northern winters were like. It was completely beyond his understanding. He did comment that a northern winter must be something like the inside of a refrigerator!

On The Island, there is actually little difference in the appearance

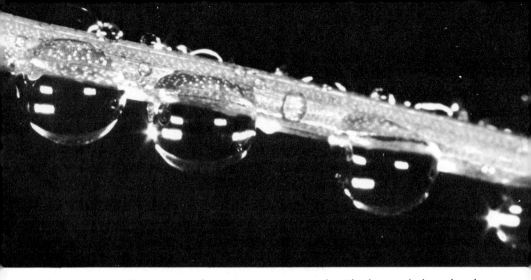

In early morning, the grasses are covered with drops of dew that hang suspended from their blades. These drops of water are forced from ducts during the night by a process called guttation.

of the forest trees in winter and summer. In winter the cypresses stand with bare limbs, as do a few other trees, the oaks and hickories. The live oaks, of course, retain their foliage all year. The pines, magnolias, and bays look the same.

With the coming of spring, soft winds blow off the nearby Gulf and the magnolias, titis, and other flowering trees come into bloom. Many birds that have spent the winter on The Island fly northward to nest. The robins are gone, migrated northward where, as Southerners often remark, "They sing for the Yankees after having enjoyed the hospitality of the South all winter!"

Summer days on The Island are like identical beads on a string; during my periodic visits, they pass one by one with but minor variations. Each morning the sun rises above the river, bathing it for a time in a pale coral glow that gradually fades away. The vegetation of The Island at this time of day is damp with droplets of dew shining like gems upon every leaf. As I walk along the grass-covered bank among the palmetto clumps my feet and legs become wet with the dew, the droplets of water forced out of the leaves and known as guttation water. The dew does not "fall." It is part of the water physiology of the plants; the jewel-like droplets appear along the margins of the leaves as if each one were set with precious stones sparkling in the morning light. During the cool island nights, pressure from the roots forces water upward through the stems and out of the leaves through special glands or ducts known as hydathodes. Guttation is the plants' means of liberating unneeded water, but to me these liquid gems have a special allure; they gleam in the rays of the sun like globular lenses and when I bring my eyes close to them I can see reflected within their spherical depths a hundred hues; they are like crystal balls foretelling the future day, promising that the sun will continue to shine. On cloudy mornings there are no droplets suspended from the leaves and at such times I walk dry-footed through the forest.

A stroll across The Island on a summer morning is always interesting and refreshing, even if nothing of major interest is seen. The forest trees stand quietly while the morning songs of birds filter down from the leafy world far above. The waters of the cypress lake sparkle in the sun, and ripple rings from feeding fish expand upon the surface. Now and again, soft plops and splashes are heard along the shore. The splashes are made by fish in the shallows but the soft plops result from bubbles of methane gas escaping from beneath the mud where it is generated by decaying organic matter. Both above and below its surface, The Island is a living thing animated by many forces.

Summer days on The Island are hot and humid; the early-morning coolness is rapidly replaced by smothering heat as the sun climbs higher in the sky where fleecy clouds chase each other toward the east. Within the confines of the dense vegetation the humidity quickly reaches the saturation point and the skin of the human explorer or traveler breaks out in sweat that soaks the clothing with moisture. When I am taking photographs, perspiration from my brow drips upon the camera's ground-glass, making focusing quite difficult. In this deep forest, plant and animal photography is complicated enough by spiny vines and the dim light.

Many years ago, when I first contemplated coming to the South to live, I recall looking in an atlas to learn something about the climate. It stated bluntly, "Climate semitropical; summers long and

Much of The Island's forest is marshy, with the trees standing in water. It has the appearance of a tropical jungle.

hot." Yet, even though reared in the cool western mountains, I have learned to love this land of my adoption; I love the heat of its noons and, most of all, its lush, green forests. I thrill to its nights, scented with magnolia and pine, and even revel in the odors of its rivers and bayous redolent of dank vegetation and fishy smells. Summer mornings on The Island are like that.

Along the margin of the lake I am often forced to detour around cypress knees and muddy areas where cottonmouth moccasins lie coiled, their dark bodies half-submerged. Here grow aquatic plants of many kinds; clumps of arrowheads, or *Sagittaria*, lift their arrow-shaped leaves above the shallow water and, in places, the surface is covered by growths of duckweed spreading out like living green carpets. In late autumn these tiny aquatic plants sink to the bottom, rising again in spring to continue their growth on the surface. Floating also upon the water are small clusters of *Azolla*, or water ferns, most unusual of all the members of the great fern tribe. Very tiny in size, the *Azolla* plants vary in color from green to rust-red and when I dip my finger among them they adhere to it and I can see that each little floating plant is complete with rootlets that hang down in the water, helping it to absorb needed food materials. The leaves are covered with water-repelling hairs that prevent the tiny plants from sinking below the surface. Long ago, the ancestors of the ferns left the water, but here is an example of one that reverted to the ancient habitat and has its leaves modified, enabling it to survive there. I am reminded of Thoreau's statement that "God made ferns to show what He could do with leaves." Always, the life-giving sun is the governing factor and every plant, the large and the small, strives toward this source of energy.

Growing somewhat beyond the reach of the water is a sow this-tle, *Sonchus*, the base of each dentate leaf clasping the central stem. When I stand above the plant, looking down upon it, I see that the leaves are arranged around the stem in such a manner as to assure each the advantage of light falling from above. Looking more closely I see that the leaves are placed upon the stem in a spiral pattern and, in an attempt to determine the "pitch" of this particular arrangement, I find that if I trace an imaginary spiral up the stem it passes the bases of five leaves while making three turns around the stem before reaching a leaf base directly above the one where the count began. Botanists would call this a 3:5 spiral. I next

Among the most unusual of all ferns is Azolla, *which floats on the surface of the water.*

examine other sow thistles growing nearby and find that each one has its leaves arranged in the same way, obviously a genetic characteristic of the plants. A number of other herbaceous plants are found to have leaf arrangements of other types, but their leaves all follow spiral paths up the stems.

As a naturalist I, of course, am familiar with that phase of botany known as phyllotaxy, which deals with leaf arrangement. If you have never given this matter much thought it is probable that you believed a plant's leaves to be placed on the stem in a more or less random arrangement, but such is far from the case. Every plant exhibits its own special type of leaf arrangement or phyllotaxy, a part of its genetic makeup that is both mysterious and astonishing.

Growing along the way are "weeds" and plants of numerous other kinds; here is a small white daisy *(Erigeron)* and when I study its flower head with my hand lens I see that the small florets are neatly arranged in spirals. But my eye actually sees two spirals, one rotating one way and one the other. A count of these spirals shows that there are twenty-one rotating in a clockwise direction and thirteen in a counterclockwise direction. This is called a 13:21 sequence and has more significance than you might at first suppose.

From about A.D. 1170 to 1250 there lived an Italian mathematician named Leonardo da Pisa, better known by his nickname "Fibonacci." Among his other accomplishments, he developed a **strange mathematical sequence of numbers** in which the sum of any

The leaves of the sow thistle (Sonchus) are arranged in a spiral up the stem. If a line is traced over the bases of the leaves it will be found that it passes over five leaves and goes three times around the stem before reaching a leaf directly above the one where the count began. Each sow thistle has this same leaf arrangement.

Here is a vertical view of a young goldenrod plant. The spiral arrangement of its leaves assures that each one will receive sufficient light.

two numbers equals the next number. It goes thus: 1, 1, 2, 3, 5, 8, 13, 21, 34, 55, 89, etc. To mathematicians, this is known as the Fibonacci Series and it often turns up in mathematical problems involving sequences and the geometry of triangles. Now, if we return to the daisy, we find that the spiral ray pattern 13:21 in its flower head falls in the Fibonacci Series as do the leaf spirals of most plants.

Here on the ground lies a pine cone fallen from a nearby tree. Its scales are open and the winged seeds it once contained have been shed. I pick it up and find, when I study the scales, that, like the florets of the daisy, they are spirally arranged. With some difficulty I determine that there are eight spirals going one way and thirteen going the other way. Thus, the scales of the pine cone follow an 8:13 sequence which, like the florets of the daisy, fall in the mysterious Fibonacci Series of numbers. Why this is so, no one seems to know. Someday, probably, geneticists will discover the reason deeply hidden within the chromosones containing the plants' genetic codes. In the meantime we can only speculate on another strange and remarkable plant characteristic.

While I am familiar with leaf phyllotaxy, I am always intrigued by it and, when afield, often find myself counting leaves and flower parts to determine their arrangement. Perhaps this is because I find it so difficult to believe that they actually follow a seemingly abstract mathematical sequence. I recall that tree limbs, too, follow definite spirals up the trunk, but when I look overhead at the various trees I find but little evidence of it. This, I am aware, is because,

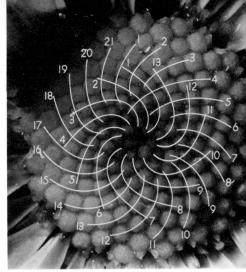

Left: *If the florets in the bloom of this daisy fleabane (Erigeron) are studied closely it will be found that they are arranged in two opposing spirals.* Right: *If opposing spirals are superimposed on the daisy it can be seen that there are twenty-one spirals rotating to the right and thirteen rotating to the left. This is called a 13:21 arrangement.*

as trees grow, some limbs are shed, leaving them in a more or less randomized arrangement.

Spiral patterns in nature are quite common, even though a little mysterious, but in the case of many plants the spiral arrangement of leaves serves a very useful purpose; it assures that the leaves will be so placed as to receive their proportionate amount of sunlight. As far as spiral patterns of animals are concerned, I do not have far to look for a good example; here on the ground is an abandoned snail shell which can be found to follow a logarithmic spiral in its convolutions.

While ruminating this morning on the growth patterns of plants and animals, I begin noticing the almost infinite shapes of the leaves of the plants and trees along the way. Some are oval, others are shaped like stars, while the margins of still others are divided and lobed in various ways. Here is a palmetto, its fan-like fronds a yard across and palmately divided into rays. Some distance away grows a sassafras tree. Its leaves are of three kinds even though they all grow on the same twig. One type is oval in shape, another has a tooth-like lobe on one side, while yet another has tooth-like lobes on each side. This leaf characteristic has resulted in the scientific

name of the tree, *Sassafras variifolium*, but what could possibly be
the value of such variation in leaf shape and how did it evolve?
Probably there is no logical answer to such questions, any more
than we can rationalize on the coloration of most birds.

A few, at least, of the characteristics of leaves do, of course, have
significance. Parrot feather, a common aquatic plant, grows with
some of its leaves submerged and others above the water's surface.
Those that grow above the water have broader rays than those
below the surface, obviously an adaptation to two different envi-
ronments. While walking in the rain I have noticed drops of water
streaming from the tips of pointed leaves. Such pointed leaftips
cause water to drain off quickly, thereby protecting the leaves from
damage. Leaves of this type are said to have "drip tips" or "drip
points" and leaves such as those of black oaks have several such
points. But lest we become too dogmatic about the value of drip
tips, let us recall the rounded forms of white oak and many other
leaves. There are numerous exceptions. Nature's patterns are not
always entirely logical and she rarely seems satisfied with simple
shapes. It is a physiological fact, however, that leaves which are cut
and divided function better than those of solid form. This is because
air flows faster over such leaves, thereby increasing their efficiency.

The shapes and forms of leaves have always fascinated me and I

Left: *The scales of a pine cone also follow an arrangement consisting of
two opposing spirals.* Right: *When two series of opposing spirals are superimposed on the pine cone it is found that it has an 8:13 arrangement or
sequence.*

find myself taking pictures of various kinds, especially the more unusual types. The negatives go into my files and someday, perhaps, I shall write a book about leaves and their design. In the meantime, I marvel at their multitudinous forms and speculate on the many remarkable ways in which they are adapted to carry out their functions.

Being especially conscious of leaves and their design, I wander on across The Island to the far shore where I have previously noticed many insectivorous plants. These plants are of special interest since their structures are so marvelous and their manners of life so incredible.

The place where these plants grow on The Island is marshy and near the shore, sloping upward toward a stand of tall pines. Scattered here and there among the semi-aquatic plants are numerous pitcher plants, their tall tube-like leaves rising somewhat above the other vegetation, each one with a hood extending over its top. They grow in clumps, several leaves arising from one root system, and I notice that several of them are still in bloom, their strange flowers bearing yellow petals hanging from the nodding heads.

Pausing beside a group of pitcher plants, I cut one off and study its structure; it is tubular in form, an inch in diameter at the top and tapering downward toward the base. Its outer walls are heavily veined and some of the veins are blood-red. Extending out over the open top is a graceful "lid," the purpose of which, no doubt, is to prevent rain from entering. The "lid," too, is veined with red. Now peering deeply down into the hollow leaf I see that it is almost completely filled with dead insects consisting mostly of moths and a few ants, all packed down tightly.

Here in my hand I hold what is probably one of the plant world's most remarkable leaves, so modified and adapted that it forms an amazingly efficient insect trap, one that not only lures insects to their dooms but also digests them and absorbs the products of the digestion for the benefit of the plant. Carefully I cut this leaf trap lengthwise with my knife, exposing the dead insects it contains. Looking closely at these I notice several fly larvae or maggots, all

Left: *The unusual blooms of pitcher plants are golden yellow. Within the hollow leaves, captured insects are killed and digested, supplying nourishment for the plant.* Right: *The tubular leaves of the pitcher plants serve as leaf traps for capturing insects. A graceful canopy extending out over the top prevents rain from entering.*

alive, living among the leaf's gruesome booty. These are the larvae of flesh flies *(Sarcophaga)* that have developed the ability to fly into the lethal traps and lay their eggs so that their larvae may feed upon the insect carrion contained within. How is it, I wonder, that these flies can live in safety where most other insects are killed and digested by the plant's lethal enzymes? In any case, these larvae do survive, a tribute to the remarkable way in which they are adapted to a special habitat, the only place where they are found.

Examining other pitcher plant specimens, I notice a few that appear to have been mutilated by some sort of leaf-feeding insect. When examined closely, I find that these pitcher plant leaves have deep grooves cut all the way around their inside surfaces just below the tops. This has caused the upper portions, that is, the portions above the groove, to die and collapse inward, thus closing the entrances. A little mystified by this discovery, I cut some of the damaged leaves open and, in each case, find a small, black caterpillar inside. These are of unusual form; along their sides are spiny tubercles, one on each segment. Apparently I have discovered still another insect that is immune to the pitcher plant's poisons.

Later, in entomological literature, I found that these little caterpillars and their habits are well known; the adults are attractive moths classified in the genus *Exyra*. Before the caterpillars pupate within the leaf pitchers—only one to each pitcher—they have the foresight to cut holes near the bottom to allow accumulated water to drain out, thus preventing the pupae from drowning.

One pitcher plant appears to have been stuffed full of fine grass and when this is removed several dead or paralyzed caterpillars are revealed along with a wasp larva. I am especially pleased to find this specimen, since I am aware that there is a caterpillar-hunting wasp that uses the cylindrical stems of pitcher plants, thus saving the labor of excavating a tunnel in the earth as do many other hunting wasps. As in the case of the caterpillar that cuts an opening near the bottom of the pitcher plant to serve as a drain, the wasp shows remarkable maternal foresight in assuring the welfare of her young by also cutting a hole to prevent the accumulation of water. A similar problem is solved by two different insects in the same manner.

In my examinations of a large number of other pitcher plants, I notice a few with small spider webs built crosswise deep within their throats. Evidently the small spiders have evolved the habit of constructing their insect-catching webs in this location, a place where insects are certainly most apt to be found. The pitcher plants seem to have attracted a number of "chiselers" who take advantage of their hospitality.

The cylindrical leaves of these plants are remarkably well fitted to carry out their function; their inner surfaces are covered with fine scales, making it very difficult for a trapped insect to crawl out once it has been lured into the leaf-pitcher by its odors. In addition, the plant secretes a narcotic substance which stupefies and eventually kills the unfortunate prey.

Higher above the water I find another type of pitcher plant, one whose leaves rest horizontally upon the ground instead of growing vertically. Each of these plants has five or six leaf traps arranged

Left: *Another kind of pitcher plant has horizontal leaves into which crawling insects are lured. (See arrow)* Right: *This cut-away view shows how insects, once within the tubular stem, are prevented from escaping by backwardly-directed spines. Trapped insects are digested.*

around a central crown. The outer end of the leaf trap resembles one end of a canoe and, when cut open, I find that just behind the prow of the "canoe" there is a small opening, one that leads into a chamber at the back of which there is yet another opening, this one leading into a passage in the hollow leaf. This passage is lined with backwardly directed spines. When a crawling insect is enticed into the first chamber, perhaps by the odor, it then seeks a means of escape and the passage on into the hollow leaf appears to be the best way out. This, of course, is a serious error since the passage becomes narrower and, at last, the insect finds itself trapped and unable to escape because of the backwardly directed spines. Here it dies and is slowly digested by the cannibal plant. How fortunate it is that these carnivorous plants are all of small size!

Similar situations are often occupied by plants with similar habits, a fact that is proved by my next discovery. Growing here and there on small patches of bare ground among the grasses are small plants that look like attractive, reddish buttons resting upon the earth. Some of them have central stalks bearing small white blooms. These plants, I am aware, are sundews, known to botanists as *Drosera*.

Found also on The Island are sundews — small, reddish plants that capture insects by means of glue-tipped tentacles. Note the gnat stuck to tentacles at lower left.

With my knife I slice out a bit of the soil with a tiny plant still attached and study it with my hand lens. This strange little sundew is rust-red in color and consists of many, spatulate-shaped leaves arranged in a rosette around a central point, each leaf covered with slender, knobbed tentacles upon which gleam droplets of sticky, glue-like substance. The sundews, like the pitcher plants, feed upon insects, but, as might be expected from their diminutive size, specialize in tiny kinds such as gnats. When a gnat is attracted to a sundew it sticks to the glue-covered tentacles and soon dies. In the meantime, the surrounding tentacles bend over the insect, securely pinning it down so that its body can slowly be digested and absorbed by the plant.

Insectivorous plants of various kinds occur in many parts of the world and in almost every conceivable situation, but those found on

The Island live mostly in marshy places near the shore, especially along the far side. Farther inland, however, is found yet another plant with somewhat similar habits. These are the butterworts, known to botanists as *Pinguicula*. Their leaves, like those of the sundews, are arranged in rosettes around central flower stems. The leaves are green and tongue-shaped and their upper surfaces are covered with glands. When a small insect becomes entangled in the mucilaginous material secreted by the glands, the edge of the leaf rolls slowly over it, pinning it down so that its body contents can be digested and absorbed. Since the leaves are green with chlorophyll they manufacture their own food and so, unlike the sundews, they are only partly dependent on an insect diet.

Intrigued by these marsh-living plants that supplement their diets by capturing insects, I recall another kind, an aquatic plant with similar habits that lives in the waters of the surrounding bayous. This is *Utricularia* or bladderwort, a more or less filamentous plant that grows submerged in the water, apparently with no attachment to the bottom. Its unique characteristic lies in the tiny, hollow bulbs attached along its stems. Around the openings into these bulbs are fine trigger hairs. When any small water creature, such as a water flea, touches these hairs, the bulb suddenly expands, sucking the luckless creature inside where it is digested.

Thus, around me along The Island's margin, little dramas are being enacted. They are silent affairs, usually unnoticed, yet they often result in the deaths of the lesser inhabitants; small creatures die that the voracious plants can live and produce seed.

Why, I wonder, have certain plants turned to carnivorous diets? Most plants contain green chlorophyll which enables them to manufacture food, using the energy of the sun. Why, then, do these plants capture and digest animal life? This is a question that has plagued biologists for a long while. The answer apparently lies in the fact that most insectivorous plants live in marshy areas where soil nitrates are deficient. Since the bodies of all animals contain large amounts of such compounds, it was, perhaps, logical to turn to partial animal diets.

It is late afternoon by the time I am satisfied with my investigations of the insectivorous plants, so I make my way back across The Island toward the houseboat. The sun has already dropped near the horizon, abandoning the deeper parts of the forest to shadow.

Suddenly, in the dim light, my eyes are attracted by pale plants growing near a pine. Thinking, at first, they are some sort of fungi, I walk over to investigate, and much to my elation I find them to be a group of Indian pipes, as unusual, in their way, as the strange plants I have just left. Grouped together upon the forest floor there are half a dozen of these plants, each about eight inches tall, pale white in color, touched here and there with pink. They are also known by other descriptive names such as "corpse plants" and

Pale, ghost-like Indian pipes (Monotropa) grow in the dim light of the island forest. Completely devoid of green chlorophyll, these strange plants obtain their nourishment from mycorrhizal fungi which, in turn, live upon the roots of pines.

"ghostflowers." Each one has a stem bearing a solitary nodding bloom at its top. Scientifically they are known as *Monotropa*, from the Greek meaning "once-turned," probably in reference to the single blooms which are bent downward so as to resemble the bowl of a pipe. Even though they are true flowering plants, like fungi they are completely devoid of green chlorophyll and so cannot manufacture their own food. Instead, these unusual and striking plants obtain their nourishment from underground mycorrhizal fungi that, in turn, live upon the roots of pines. This, indeed, is a strange relationship but one that might, perhaps, be expected from such unusual-looking plants. Only a few times in my career as a biologist has it been my good fortune to see these remarkable plants growing in their native habitats in pine forests. The other times were in the Great Smoky Mountains where they grew in the coniferous forest at high altitude.

I find other examples of semi-parasitic plant life growing near the Indian pipes. These are coral-root orchids, and from even a casual examination it is apparent that some sort of similarity exists. Most people think of orchids in terms of the showy greenhouse kinds used in corsages, not realizing that there are many native kinds. The greenhouse orchids are all of tropical origin; in their native habitats they grow attached to trees, often high above the ground. Here in the United States there are also small epiphytic or tree-living orchids, but they are all confined to the Everglades of Florida.

There are several kinds of small ground-living orchids on The Island, but the coral-root orchids are the most interesting since they, like the Indian pipes, absorb most of their nourishment from mycorrhizal fungi in the ground. There are several specimens grouped closely together, the stems pale pinkish in color and bearing small reddish blooms. Again like the Indian pipes, they are devoid of green chlorophyll. While their manner of growth is unusual, the chief thing I find interesting about these orchids is their means of pollination.

Extending downward from the central portion of each bloom is

Upon the damp ground in the forest gloom grow orchids of several kinds, pollinated by night-flying moths.

a flat lip, spotted with deep reddish purple, above which are two anther sacs containing packets of pollen grains. These packets are called pollinia.

Coral-root orchids, like most other native kinds, depend on night-flying moths for pollination; when a moth is attracted to a bloom and inserts its mouthparts into it in an effort to reach the nectar, its eyes come in contact with the adhesive pollinia which stick to them. When the moth flies away it carries the pollinia along, still glued to its eyes. When the moth visits another orchid bloom the pollinia are rubbed off onto the plant's stigmatic surface, thus bringing about cross-pollination.

In a little experiment, I push the head of a match into the bloom against the adhesive pollen sacs and am pleased to find, when the match is removed, that two pollinia are firmly attached to it. To determine how strongly they are cemented to the match head, I try to brush them off with a blade of grass; they remain firmly attached.

As in the case of most orchids, the seeds of the coral-roots are almost microscopic in size and require long periods under very special conditions for germination.

The tricks used by plants to assure cross-pollination are almost endless, running the gamut from wind transportation to the use of birds. Some trees and grasses depend on wind for pollen transfer and, in such plants, colorful blooms are absent. Probably the great majority of flowers are pollinated by flying insects such as bees, butterflies, and moths. Bee-pollinated flowers are of various colors, except red, since most of these insects are red-blind. Butterfly-pollinated flowers are usually red or orange, while moth-pollinated flowers are white, since white flowers can be seen best in the dusk. There are several kinds of small orchids besides the coral-roots on The Island, all with white blooms and hence dependant on moths.

At several places there are jack-in-the-pulpits (*Arisaema*), especially in damp, shady locations. These plants bear erect, green blooms somewhat resembling pitcher plants and, in a way, their functions are similar since they "capture" tiny flies. I cut away one side of a jack-in-the-pulpit bloom, the green spathe, to reveal the

Jack-in-the-pulpits thrive in the forest. Small flies are trapped in the hollow spathe for their aid in pollination.

erect, rod-like spadix at the base of which are located the flower's reproductive parts. These flowers, I am aware, depend upon small flies for pollination and I am pleased to discover several of them more or less imprisoned within the base of the sheath-like spathe. Having been lured into the bloom by a perfume especially attractive to them, the flies cannot easily escape; at least they are trapped long enough to buzz about, becoming well dusted with pollen before finding their way out. Once out, they are so foolish as to be attracted into other jack-in-the-pulpits where their adhering pollen is rubbed off on the female organs.

These peculiar little plants belong to an unusual family—the arums—which occur mostly in the Tropics where certain kinds reach enormous size. One type found in Sumatra has a bloom taller than a man. Arums of several varieties are often grown in homes and greenhouses; examples are philodendron and calla lily. Another is the voodoo lily *(Sauromatum)*. This so-called lily, like its cousin, the little jack-in-the-pulpit, lures flies into its spathe by means of odors which, while repulsive to us, are most attractive to the insects. What is of unusual interest, however, is the fact that, when ready

Reindeer moss, a lichen, grows in spongy clumps on the moist ground. This is the same lichen found in Arctic regions.

to be pollinated, the plant generates a considerable amount of heat, causing the volitalization of its perfume. It has been found that such a plant's temperature may rise nearly 70° F. during this time!

On the ground, a short distance beyond the jack-in-the-pulpits, I find another type of unusual plant, but in this case, its unique character is due chiefly to geographical range or world distribution. Scattered about over a shady area are greenish gray masses of spongy material, each about six inches across. When examined closely it can be seen that each one is made up of a fine network of branching strands. The clumps are easily removed from the ground since they have but little attachment.

What I have found in this tropical setting is a growth of reindeer moss, believe it or not! And what is so astonishing is the fact that this is the same plant found in Lapland and other cold Arctic countries, where it forms the normal food of reindeer. These gray-green clumps are classified as a lichen, *Cladonia rangiferina*, and, like other lichens, are composite plants, being made up of an alga and a fungus that are so closely associated as to appear and grow as one plant. Lichens of other types grow attached to trees everywhere on The Island and are not at all related to the true green mosses that grow in damp places. Probably no other plant has as wide a range as reindeer moss unless it is certain free-living algae or fungi. It is reported to be fairly common as far southward as Florida.

Early one hot morning I sat on the shady side of the boat drinking a last cup of coffee while hoping for a breeze that never appeared. The normal sounds of the river seemed hushed and the songs of cicadas, even at this early hour, drifted out of the nearby forest. When cicadas sing early in the morning one can usually rest assured that the coming day will be torrid. While sipping the coffee, I notice a dead crab lying on the deck. It has been captured in a crab trap during the night and, since it has been dead for several hours, is no longer fit for food. I pick up the lifeless specimen and examine it, noting how remarkably well its body parts are constructed. Each leg is hinged in a certain precise manner, the hind ones modified into oar-like flippers for propelling the creature through the water. But it is the large forelegs bearing pincers that attract my special interest. The pincers, as I know from sad past experience, are very powerful and can cause serious injury and pain if the living animal is carelessly handled. With my fingers I open and close a pincer of the now-dead crab and study the hinge mechanism. I obtain a knife and dissect away the outer wall of the shell-like claw in an effort to discover how it works. This takes considerable effort since the chitinous shell is extremely hard.

Having removed a section of the claw's side, I reveal a mass of muscles, their fibers extending inward where they are attached to two plate-like tendons, the smaller of which is connected to the base of the movable finger of the claw just above the hinge. The larger tendon is attached to the opposite side of the hinge in such a manner that the contraction of the muscles can exert great power in bringing the claw together. Thus, just as in the case of our own bodies, there are two opposing sets of muscles, a smaller one to open

Crabs are common in the waters surrounding The Island. Their front legs are armed with powerful pincers.

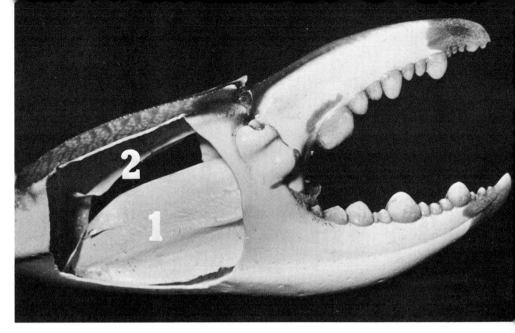

If the wall of the crab's pincer is removed, the mechanism by which it operates can be seen. The large plate (1) is attached to the base of the movable "finger" below its hinge. Muscles, extending from the plate to the wall of the pincer, enable it to exert great pressure. The "finger" is opened by muscles attached to a smaller plate (2).

the claw and a more powerful set to close it. Here is revealed the mechanics of the crab's powerful grip, to my own satisfaction, at least. This is the same mechanical principle found in the legs of insects, such as the jumping legs of the grasshoppers.

And so my periodic visits to The Island during summer pass quietly. Heat and humidity bring languor, dampening to some extent my enthusiasm for biological investigation. Yet, I am always astonished that, on such a small area of land, there are so many things to see, a truism that holds good for almost any wild place.

Chapter 7

THE CYPRESS LAKE

THERE IS SOMETHING about a deep cypress swamp that always captivates me. Perhaps this is because I grew up in a cold, northern climate where there were no such places. In many ways, a cypress swamp in the Deep South is strange, fantastic, and unreal, and the novelty of exploring one never wears off for me. I can imagine that I am in darkest Africa or in the valley of the Amazon and the sudden appearance of a leopard or monkey would surprise me not at all.

Near the center of The Island lies such a swamp consisting of several acres of open water surrounded by a dense growth of bald cypress, tupelo gum, and buttonbush (*Cephalanthus*). The swollen buttresses of the gums and cypresses rise out of the coffee-colored water like solid columns, their crowns reaching well above the surrounding forest. From some of the trees hang trumpet vines (*Tecoma radicans*) with scarlet blooms, and from every limb, as usual, sway the gray-green streamers of Spanish moss. Closer to the water's edge grows an impenetrable tangle of buttonbushes which, in spring, are covered by white globular flower-heads that are usually surrounded by bumblebees and butterflies.

Most spectacular, though, are the great gums and cypresses grow-

In and surrounding the cypress lake grow great cypresses, their swollen bases affording support in the soft ground. The high humidity favors a heavy growth of Spanish moss.

Along the lake's margins, at several points, grow button-bushes (Cephalanthus) bearing white, pincushion-like blooms.

Below: *In autumn, many trees shed their leaves which float upon the surface for a time, then sink and decay, adding organic matter to the water and staining it brown.*

ing with their roots in the soft muck where their expanded bases find anchorage and support in the moist habitat. The quiet water of the lake mirrors the trees that surround it and only now and again is the glassy surface disturbed by foraging fish. On a quiet summer day there are no sounds drifting out of the island forest except the calls of birds and the songs of insects. Autumn brings cooler weather and falling leaves. Then, with each gust of wind, additional leaves break away from their points of attachment and drift down upon the water like brightly colored scraps of paper. Red and gold, they dot the still surface and remain floating for a time, then sink to the bottom where they decompose, adding their organic matter to the mud and imparting a brown coloration to the water.

Of all the trees, the cypresses are by far the most eye-catching and spectacular as well as the best fitted to growth in water. In order to remain standing against winds, their bases are greatly expanded and solidly placed. It is, indeed, remarkable and a tribute to the way in which they are adapted that such large trees can remain standing against the force of high winds. Deep within the soft soil, the roots spread out a great distance in every direction, interlocking with the roots of the surrounding trees and forming a network that effectively resists the wind. Most unusual is the manner by which the roots of the cypresses obtain air. Surrounding the cypresses are numerous "knees" arising from the roots like round-topped cones, often extending above the water for several feet. While these "knees" are usually conical, their forms are almost infinite; many of them take on multispired shapes and, in imagination, I see among them weird representations of castles and turrets of grotesque and improbable form.

Cypress "knees" are called *pneumatophores* and they arise by localized growth that adds thick layers of wood to the upper surfaces of the roots, producing upward bends or loops. If a cypress "knee" is sawed lengthwise, it can be seen that the grain of the wood composing them has been expanded upward. It seems obvious that the function of these unique structures is that of obtaining air for the submerged roots, yet not all botanists agree. Some author-

Bubbles of marsh gas or methane escape from beneath the lake's stagnant water where it is generated by the decay of organic matter. The bursting bubbles make plopping sounds.

ities believe that they merely arise on parts of the roots which are better aerated and that their purpose is not really the obtaining of air. Regardless of the scientific explanation for the presence of cypress "knees" they are very porous and are evidently concerned in some fashion with root aeration. A common feature of deep cypress swamps and cypress-lined bayous, they add a characteristic, and often spooky, aspect to such places.

At one end of the island lake is a marshy area where, for some reason or other, the "knees" have grown to enormous proportions; they are conical in shape and average five feet in height and about the same across their bases. Strangely, about half of these "knees" have openings or cavities in their sides, giving them the appearance of small tepees or wigwams. The first time I visited this area and glimpsed these unusual "knees," I thought I had found the homes of forest gnomes, so much did they resemble some sort of subhuman habitation. What forces combined to create these peculiar cypress growths, I have no idea. I have never seen them elsewhere.

On the north side of this cypress lake a section of higher ground overlooks the water which is screened by buttonbushes. It is on this vantage point that I have spent many of my most interesting and rewarding hours on The Island. Here I constructed a rough blind of brown burlap and camouflaged its front with twigs. An obser-

vation hole was cut in the cloth and all the higher bushes removed
between the blind and the water's edge. Through the opening in
the blind I have an unobstructed view of almost the entire lake and
can watch the goings-on of the wild inhabitants without being seen.
At first they were chary of the blind but after a few days paid no
attention to it.

By means of a 20-power telescope mounted on a tripod I found
that I could sweep the entire visual field and study in detail anything that moved on or around the lake. It was, I found, something
like being invisible. I could watch a snowy egret wading in the shallow water and see its eyes as it searched for frogs and minnows. In
effect, I was there beside the attractive bird and almost felt that I
could reach out and touch it with my hand. The powerful lens gave
me a ringside seat to the little dramas enacted in the lake's environs.

From this observation point I have watched wood ducks nesting
high in holes in the trees and have seen the downy ducklings scram-
bling out of the nesting holes and swimming away with their

Water birds of many kinds
feed in the cypress lake or
wade sedately in the shallows. Some kinds nest in the
surrounding trees. Here, a
black-crowned night heron
poses at the lake's edge.

Snow-white egrets perch in trees or wade through the waters of the cypress lake spearing minnows or frogs.

mother. I have had a ringside seat to pileated woodpeckers chiseling square nest holes in dead snags far above the lake's tranquil surface and studied in close-up detail their feeding habits. As if with seven-league boots, I have swept the lens across the lake to watch musk-rats emerging from the water carrying mussel shells which they broke open on the bank to devour the fleshy mollusks contained inside. On quiet afternoons, I have also watched muskrats gathering grass and carrying it in bundles to their dens. Too, I have seen great alligator snapping turtles searching the shallows for food, their dome-shaped shells half-submerged as they moved slowly about like antediluvian monsters. They are one of the most interesting of the island's inhabitants, and second in size only to the true alligator among the reptiles that inhabit the lake. These enormous turtles, often weighing more than a hundred pounds, have heads as large as a dog's and jaws whose cutting edges can slice through a broom handle or sever a man's finger. Their body is heavy and muscular and the shell or carapace covering the back bears keels or elevated ridges. The cold reptilian eyes, sunken in the head, are alert. A cornered specimen awaits only the chance of snapping out at its tormenter. Now and then they come to the surface to breathe through their snout-like nostrils. Sometimes, on summer days, they visit the shallow estuaries where they walk about in the mud. In spring they bury their spherical eggs in the sandbars that extend along the banks, leaving them to the sun's heat for incubation. They fear no enemy and no other marsh inhabitant would dare attack a full-grown individual. Perhaps they live for a hundred years, perhaps two hundred—who knows? They lead unhurried, sluggish lives. They have no need to go anywhere; their food, in truth, usually comes to them, so there is no necessity for them to hunt. When hungry, which is almost always, an alligator snapper rests upon the bottom, half-obscured by the coffee-colored water. With vicious jaws wide open, a pink, fleshy appendage resembling a worm is extended from the floor of the mouth and moved about in an enticing manner. The snapper plays a waiting game and eventually some unwary fish approaches, attracted by the worm-like appendage. The great reptile's jaws snap shut like a steel trap, slicing cleanly through the fish's body. The remainder of the meal is devoured at leisure. Another silent drama of the lake has been enacted and the turtle settles down again to await the coming of more game while its meal is being slowly digested and assimilated.

During winter, while cold winds blow across The Island, the tur-

Above: *Soft-shelled turtles are common inhabitants of the lake and of the surrounding bayous. They rest below the water's surface with only their elongate noses protruding.* Below: *Cooter turtles swim just beneath the surface or sun themselves on bars and floating logs.*

tles all lie hidden in the mud, deep in the sleep of hibernation. Theirs is a pleasant life. They know nothing of winter; at its approach they bury themselves in the mud where they remain until spring returns to warm the waters of the bayous and the lake. In March they appear as if by magic upon their accustomed sunning places, logs and exposed sandbars. One spring morning I was so fortunate as actually to see an alligator snapping turtle emerging from hibernation; it rose to the lake's surface still bearing a heavy layer of mud on its back. Once awakened from the winter's lethargy, turtles of all kinds assemble, absorbing the sun's heat which speeds up the development of the eggs contained within their cold bodies. The alligator snappers do not take part in these sun baths; they remain aloof from the assemblages of their lesser relatives, the cooters and mud turtles. But soon they all deposit their eggs in the earth or sand of the bars and banks. When the young emerge they are small and defenseless, falling easy prey to many predators. Yet, as usual, nature balances her books; more eggs are laid than marsh and lake can support. Enemies remove the surplus and the turtle population remains about the same from year to year and from century to century.

One of the various reptiles of the cypress lake is the mud snake (*Farancia abacura*), often known locally as the "stinging snake." Once, while walking along the lake's margin, I captured one of these snakes as it was crawling slowly over the mud. It was about four feet in length and its back was slate color with its belly marked by bright red crossbars. When held firmly in my hand it thrashed about, striking my arm several times so hard that its sharp tail drew a drop or two of blood. It made no attempt to bite; in fact, it hid its head within the coils of its muscular body.

Closely examing the tip of its tail, I noticed that it tapered to a very sharp point. This pointed tail, coupled with the fact that the snake actually strikes with it, has given rise to the local belief that it carries a sting. There is, of course, no sting in the tail and no venom and so the mud snake is virtually harmless.

Early one summer morning I secreted myself in the blind and

The mud snake or "stinging snake" (Farancia) lives in and around the lake, sometimes burrowing in the mud. It may often reach six feet in length, its food consisting of salamanders and earth worms. It strikes with its sharp tail, but the tail contains no sting.

settled down to await developments. The sun was already hot and the surrounding forest reverberated with the sound of cicadas. A pair of snowy egrets waded about along the opposite side of the lake, their white bodies in striking relief against the darker shore. Through the telescope I watched dragonflies perched on cypress "knees" and could even see them move their heads as they scanned their surroundings for enemies and prey. Their abdomens pulsated with respiratory movements.

One arm of the lake was hidden from my view because of the trees and I had about decided that it was going to be a dull morning with nothing out of the ordinary when my eyes were attracted by something moving in the water of the estuary beyond the screening trees. As I watched, a group of twenty-five wood storks walked into view from beyond the point of land. This was indeed out of the ordinary since these birds, our only true storks, are not at all common; I had seen only one or two living birds previously.

Wood storks *(Mycteria americana)* are not pretty birds by any stretch of the imagination, as is evidenced by their other common names, which include gourdhead, blue Charley, and plumber. In some localities they are also called wood "ibises." They stand about a yard tall and their plumage is white with greenish black markings on wings and tail coverts. The birds would be quite attractive, however, were it not for their heads and necks which are bluish in color and devoid of feathers. Their bills are their most distinctive features. About nine inches long, they curve downward, imparting a somewhat doleful appearance. The scientific name, *Mycteria*, is of Greek origin meaning "turned-up nose," a misnomer since the bill is actually turned *downward*.

The group of wood storks I saw in the lake were wading along in the shallow water with heads lowered so that their bills were submerged. As they walked about, they trailed their bills along beside their feet, not in front. Now and then I noticed that they appeared to have captured something but was unable to see what it was. Later, I read that their food consists of frogs, fishes, small snakes, and even young alligators.

These large water birds were formerly more abundant than they are now and so it is not surprising that Audubon had ample oppor-

Wood storks, often called gourd-heads, visit the lake where they feed upon fishes, frogs, and other small aquatic animals. When alarmed, they spiral out of sight in the sky.

tunity to observe them in their native habitat. He wrote of them, "This species feeds entirely on fish and aquatic reptiles of which it destroys an enormous quantity. To secure its food, the wood ibis walks through shallow muddy lakes or bayous in numbers. As soon as they have discovered a place abounding in fish they dance, as it were, all through it until the water becomes thick with the mud stirred from the bottom. . . . The fishes, on rising to the surface, are instantly struck by the beaks of the birds. . . . When digestion is partially accomplished, they take to the wing, rise in spiral circlings to an immense height."

I watched these great birds for more than an hour as they fed in the shallow water of the lake. Then, perhaps alarmed by my presence, they took off with a loud flapping of their wings which beat the air with powerful strokes. When airborne, they circled over the lake with their long necks stretched forward and their legs extended rigidly to the rear. They disappeared behind the tall trees to my left and, since I hoped to have another look at them, I walked down to the lake's edge for a better view. Much to my surprise, the wood storks were nowhere in sight; seemingly they had simply disappeared into thin air. Where they had gone remained a mystery until I returned home and looked up references on their habits. Audubon and other writers, I found, had recorded how these birds begin circling higher and higher into the sky and eventually pass out of sight at great altitude. Apparently this is what happened to the birds at the lake. On succeeding days I saw the wood storks several times and they usually repeated the performance of spiraling out of sight when alarmed as they had done on the first morning.

Late one afternoon, after watching the wood storks again for several hours, I was preparing to leave. At this moment I detected a flash of pink in the air over the far side of the lake. Thinking it to be only an egret, its white feathers tinted red by the sunset, I turned away. Then I looked again and discovered, to my intense delight, that the bird was a roseate spoonbill, its wings and back bright pink as it came into a graceful landing in the shallow water. It carefully folded its wings and began feeding among the cypress "knees" and I could clearly see its spoon-shaped bill as it probed for food consisting, I knew, of insects and other aquatic life.

Once in the water with its wings folded, the bird's bright pink coloration was not as evident as when on the wing but, nevertheless, it was truly a pretty sight and I was grateful that I had seen it. After watching the spoonbill for some time from behind the blind, I stood up. At once the bird took to the wing and again I was astonished by its vivid coloration, strongly accentuated against the dark green of the distant, shadowy forest. It disappeared beyond the moss-draped cypresses like some gay figment of an active imagination, and I paused to wonder if I had actually seen a large, flame-hued bird flying gracefully over the somber waters of the island lake.

Often, when I am away from The Island, I close my eyes and imagine that I am seated again in the blind. I see the panorama of lake and surrounding forest and thrill to the sights and sounds of that wild place. In my mind's eye I can visualize the wood storks wading sedately in the quiet lake and hear the beating of their wings as they take to the air amid sprays of sparkling water. I see again a great pink bird sailing across the water and hear the calls of woodland birds from the deeper forest. These are things not soon forgotten and I live them over again and again.

A naturalist watches and waits and his reward is in the things he sees and feels. From the seclusion of the blind I have watched the play of life of many kinds—alligators cruising along the surface of the lake and coots feeding among the cypress "knees." Strangest, perhaps, of all the things I have seen was the "rolling" of spoonbill catfish on the lake's still surface.

Known to science as *Polydon spathula*, the spoonbill catfish, or paddlefish, is one of our unusual native fishes. Actually it is not a catfish at all, being more closely related to such primitive fish as the sturgeons and gars. In addition to other peculiarities, it is our lone representative of a family of fishes whose only other relatives are found in such Chinese rivers as the Yangtze and Hwang-ho. Probably these fish once had a world-wide distribution, but now only two species survive in widely separated areas of the world.

The paddlefish is unusual even in appearance; its body is free of scales and attached to the front of its head is a long, thin, blade-like snout apparently used by the creature for stirring up the mud in its search for food. In a way, the feeding habits of these fish resemble those of the whale since it obtains its nourishment by straining food out of water which passes in enormous quantities through its large gill slits. One writer states very aptly that a paddlefish is actually "a living plankton net." It feeds in muddy water which is said to be stirred up by its "bill," yet so efficient is its straining mechanism of fine, comb-like gill rakers that no mud reaches its intestines. The food strained out of the water and mud consists of insect larvae and other small items of aquatic life.

Except for sturgeons, these are the largest fish occurring in the vicinity of The Island. I have seen specimens nearly six feet in length and weighing, I would guess, about 150 pounds. The record is said to be 173 pounds. While immature paddlefish have been captured, very little is known about their breeding habits.

One summer day while again seated in the blind at the cypress lake I was surprised to see paddlefish in the act of "rolling," a strange habit that seems to have no explanation. The fish would shoot completely out of the water in graceful arcs and slip back below the surface, creating very little disturbance. After one or two started, paddlefish would suddenly begin this so-called "rolling" all over the lake, then none would be seen for as long as ten minutes. Suddenly, here and there over the lake, they would appear again. What was it, I wondered, that triggered this peculiar jumping or "rolling"? As far as I have been able to find, authorities do not know; it is merely another of the riddles relating to these strange fish.

At the opposite end of the scale, with regard to size, are the top minnows, or *Gambusia*, small fish that are abundant in the waters of the island lake as well as in the surrounding bayous. At almost every point along the shore, schools of these minnows can be seen busily foraging for mosquito larvae and other prey. They swim with ease in water less than a half inch in depth in their insatiable hunt for

Gambusia, or top minnows, feed along the water's surface where they subsist on mosquito larvae and other aquatic insects. Like guppies, they produce live offspring. The swollen abdomens of these specimens indicate pregnancy.

living food and, for this reason, are regarded as man's ally in his eternal battle against mosquitoes.

Most remarkable of the top minnow's habits are those connected with its reproduction. In most fish, fertilization of the eggs is external; that is, the female lays her eggs which are then fertilized by the male. By contrast, the male top minnow has its anal fin modified into a copulatory organ by which sperm is transferred into the female's reproductive ducts, thereby fertilizing the eggs while still carried by her. These fertilized eggs develop within the body of the minnow, and the young are born alive and immediately able to shift for themselves; in fact, if they do not at once seek shelter, the female will devour them, which certainly emphasizes the lack of any mother instinct in her character. Pregnant females are easily identified by their great swollen abdomens. The males are smaller than the females and their anal fins are slender.

These common little members of the fish tribe belong to the same family as guppies, the Poeciliidae, and their reproductive habits are quite similar. Like guppies, they live well in an aquarium; I once kept half a dozen specimens for over five years and, I must admit, gave them very little attention. The name, top minnows, is very descriptive, since they cruise about just beneath the surface, always on the hunt for food. Probably they are the most prolific of all our native fishes. They also occur in Cuba and it was there that they received their original name *Gambusina*, a term meaning "of little value," which is unfair since it is now known that they are important factors in the suppression of such mosquito-borne diseases as yellow fever and malaria.

It is in the waters of this cypress lake that the distant past meets the present, where the descendants of ancient fishes mingle with more modern kinds. One of the more archaic is the bowfin or grindle, sometimes known locally by its French name, *choupique*. The name, bowfin, is very apt since the fish's dorsal fin extends almost all the way down its back in a curving contour and there is a dark "eyespot" at the base of the tail in the case of the male.

One quiet afternoon for some unknown reason, I decided to try my luck at fishing in the cypress lake, using live minnows as bait. As usual in my case, luck was against me and I had about decided that I should stick to biological investigations when there was a tremendous tug on my line and the pole was almost jerked from my hands. I had no idea what sort of fish I had hooked so I "played" it carefully and was at last able to land an eighteen-inch bowfin. It had put up a good fight, compared to the usual game fish. The bowfin is not edible so I returned it to the lake.

Bowfins are quite common in the waters of the area and have some most unorthodox habits. When the water becomes deficient in oxygen, the bowfin uses its swim-bladder as a sort of lung; it rises to the surface of the water and breathes air. Many fish have swim-bladders, thin membranous air sacs contained within their abdominal cavities which serve as hydrostatic organs enabling them to maintain their depth in the water. In most fish, however, the swim-bladders have no external openings through the throat; the bowfin is an exception. This strange fish is also able to burrow into the mud of dried-up lakes or ponds and survive for long periods by means of its air-breathing capabilities; bowfins have sometimes been plowed up in fields that had previously been flooded. In this

Fish of many kinds inhabit the cypress lake. The long-eared sunfish is common.

respect, they resemble the lungfishes of Australia and Africa which have the same ability to survive drought.

Another rather unusual characteristic of the bowfin is found in its nesting habits; in spring the male excavates a shallow nest in the mud in which the female deposits her eggs. When they hatch, the male guards the young until they are about four inches long. On several occasions I have seen the little bowfins swarming about males like clusters of bees in the shallow water among the cypress "knees." The bowfin may not be a particularly attractive fish, but it does have this one commendable trait.

There are numerous other fish in the cypress lake, including sunfish of various kinds, some of beautiful, golden coloration. Gars, too, occur there and I have often seen them sculling along just beneath the surface. One evening just before dusk, while perched on a cypress stump above the water, I saw a large gar rise from the depths of the lake like a surfacing submarine; I estimated it to be at least six feet long and could clearly see its elongate snout which I knew to be armed with rows of needle-like teeth, well fitted for tearing flesh. This specimen was no doubt the alligator gar, *Lepisosteus spatula*, which is quite common in southern lakes and rivers. It differs from the longnose gar, *L. osseus*, by its shorter and heavier snout, but all gars are heavily armored with flint-like, enameled scales set closely together like chain mail, making them almost bulletproof. I once shot several times at a large gar with a .22-caliber rifle but, as far as I could determine, the bullets did not penetrate

Left: *A gar's body is covered with flint-like scales set close together, protecting the fish with a covering of flexible armor. Right: If the scales are removed from a gar's body, it can be seen how they are joined together into a mosaic that protects the fish. Gar scales were once used as arrowheads by the Indians.*

its body. As an indication of the hardness of gar scales it may be mentioned that they were once used as arrowheads by Indians. They vary in shape, depending on the part of the body from which they come; some are diamond-shaped while others resemble typical arrowheads with cutting edges. When attached to the fish, they fit together in a mosaic that affords excellent protection against enemies.

There are many unusual things about gars that set them apart from most other fish. It is said that their eggs or roe are poisonous, though I cannot speak with authority on this. In any case, they lay an enormous number of eggs; a forty-inch female may deposit up to thirty-six thousand. Apparently the eggs are attached to sticks and are resistant to drying. On several occasions, I have seined the two-inch young in shallow water and noted that they were close miniatures of the adults, complete with needle-sharp teeth set in slender snouts. Even at this tender age they are voracious little beasts, feeding upon small creatures.

The gar is able to breathe air in a manner similar to that of the bowfin. While it has gills like other fish, it can also breathe air into its swim-bladder, enabling it to live in warm, stagnant waters where dissolved oxygen is scant. On hot summer days gar fish may often be seen rising to the surface of the lake, their long snouts breaking the water as they roll to one side while expelling and gulping in air. Sometimes, also, on hot days they lie asleep or motionless on the water's surface like floating logs. In a manner of speaking, gars are living fossils; by most rules, they should have become extinct millions of years ago, along with the other armored fishes of ancient seas. Yet, they have lived on, sluggish, stealthy and powerful, preying upon other fish. Today, they occur only in North and Central America. It has been said with much truth that the gars are the sharks of our fresh waters since they have shark-like habits; they devour many of the lesser creatures of the marshland and bayous, but are especially predaceous on muskrats.

Because of their voracious natures it might seem that human swimmers would be in danger of attack by gars but, so far, I know of no such occurrence. There was one incident at Mandeville, Louisiana, many years ago that may indicate that encounters with gars may not be without danger. A nine-year-old girl was sitting at the edge of Lake Ponchartrain with her feet dangling in the water. Her brother, age thirteen, was several feet away. The little girl screamed and when her brother came to her assistance he saw that her leg was covered with blood. According to her statement, a large fish had grabbed her leg but she had been able to drive it off by striking it with her hand. One thumb was scratched in the encounter. The boy saw the fish—he identified it as a gar—and said that it was about seven feet long. The little girl received medical attention and the attending physician stated that "the wounds were all superficial and looked as if they were made with coarse needles inserted in a board." Certainly an attack by a gar would leave such wounds.

The presence of the varied population of fish in the island lake

The snout of the gar is armed with formidable teeth, enabling it to capture other fish. Gars are also enemies of muskrats and small animals, and there is one case on record of a large gar attacking a child.

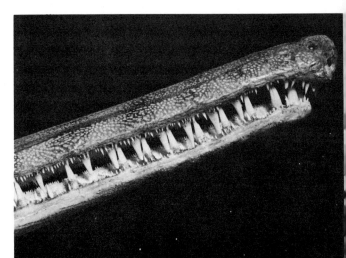

brings up an interesting question: how did they get there? The land surrounding the water is considerably above the levels of both the river and bayous and I have never seen the water high enough to flow into or out of the lake. There are many isolated lakes and ponds in this vicinity, especially on the mainland, and in almost every instance they contain fish of one or more kinds. The local explanation is that they "rained down." Now this may seem pre-posterous but let's look into the matter a little more closely.

In scientific literature, there are many well-substantiated cases of rains of living fishes, some of which go back for hundreds of years. The afternoon of May 18, 1928, was a typical spring day on the cotton farm of W. L. Doughtie, situated about twelve miles east of Tarboro, North Carolina. The skies had been threatening and about 3 P.M. Mr. Doughtie hurried to the barn to put up his team. Having accomplished this chore, he started toward the house in the rain, which by then was falling in torrents. Something cold and slick struck Mr. Doughtie in the face, causing him to look up; it was raining large numbers of small fish from two to three inches in length! After the shower, many of the fish were observed swim-ming about in puddles of rainwater.

The above incident is not an isolated case; many more could be cited. There is at least one record of a waterspout being observed and a resulting shower of fish occurring nearby. This was at Boca Ciega Bay, Florida. The waterspout was seen over the bay and, shortly thereafter, hundreds of small fish rained down on a nearby golf course.

Probably the best substantiated rain of fishes, and one that I personally investigated, occurred at Marksville, Louisiana, on the morning of October 23, 1947. What lends credibility to this inci-dent is that a United States Government fisheries biologist, A. D. Bajkov, was present, eating breakfast in a local restaurant. Be-tween seven and eight o'clock, fish ranging from two to nine inches in length fell in the streets and in the yards. Mr. Bajkov collected a number of the fish and, later, preserved them in formalin. The biggest specimen was a large-mouth bass measuring nine and a quarter inches long; all were absolutely fresh and fit for human consumption and many were alive. Mr. Bajkov's investigation showed that the "rain" of fishes covered an area approximately one thousand feet long and about seventy-five feet wide. The weather was comparatively calm in the immediate vicinity but numerous small tornadoes had been sighted some distance away. I looked into this case several years later and interviewed local residents. They stated that most of the fish fell in private yards, in the courthouse square, and near the Union Bank. At least fifty fish were picked up, many of them still alive. Some local citizens placed a few of the fish in refrigerators as proof of the unusual incident. I am convinced of the authenticity of this strange occurrence.

Once again, we arrive at the conclusion that there are many things about nature which are but little understood. Is this the explanation for the presence of fishes of many kinds in the waters of the island lake and in other isolated bodies of water? Certainly it is as reasonable an assumption as any; the fish are there and they arrived in some fashion; fish do not fly or walk.

The vicinity of the cypress lake, for some reason or other, is favorable to the construction of spiders' webs. The surrounding forest is more or less open at ground level, providing avenues between the towering tree trunks across which large spider webs are often built. Early this morning, on my way to the blind, I was forced to detour around several enormous webs constructed by *Nephila* spiders.

These spiders are most unusual in appearance, as are the webs they build. *Nephila* spiders are quite large; their bodies are the size of a man's thumb and variously marked with golden spots and stripes. But it is their legs that at once attract attention, since they are set at the joints with tufts of hair, making one think of a French-poodle. While these spiders are conspicuous in appearance, it is their webs that are unique; they are constructed of gold-colored silk! Of all the world's spiders, the *Nephilas* are the only ones that spin webs with golden silk. Previous to my visits to The Island, I had seen *Nephila* spiders preserved in alcohol but their colors had faded and

Building its large webs of gold-colored silk, the Nephila *spider is common near the cypress lake. The body of this huge spider is marked with yellow. There are tufts of hairs on its legs.*

I knew nothing about their ways; thus I was pleased to find them in their natural habitat. Most of the *Nephila* webs I found on The Island were about chest-high, but I have seen a few as much as twenty feet above the ground. In most cases the large webs were at an angle from the vertical, with the spiders resting at their centers. If disturbed, the spiders cause the webs to vibrate rapidly back and forth. According to spider literature, the males build no webs and are much smaller than their mates, but I have rarely seen them.

Most orb-weaving spiders build their silken snares during quiet summer evenings and they are used but one night; by dawn they are in tatters as the result of the morning breezes which tear them apart. By contrast, *Nephila* webs are built of stronger silk and are used during several nights for snaring insects. I have watched the females as they went about the laborious task of making repairs. Since the webs are used more than once and are periodically repaired, they often look quite ragged.

In spinning their webs, *Nephila* spiders actually use silk of two different colors; the viscid strands that spiral around the web are bright golden yellow, while the other lines are of white or colorless silk. If the golden strands are examined under a hand lens it is seen that they are strung with droplets of sticky glue, giving them their adhesive quality.

Spider silk is very strong and durable and that produced by *Nephila* spiders is no exception. Because of its beautiful golden hue, an attempt was once made to exploit it commercially. These spiders are especially abundant in the Malagasy Republic, where a complete set of bed drapes was actually produced and later exhibited in Paris, but the project was never successful, largely because the spiders will eat only living insects which were difficult to obtain in sufficient quantities.

Spiders of many other kinds are present on The Island but, in most cases, are of the usual types. Wolf spiders run about over the forest floor in search of insect game, while orb-weaving spiders of various sorts spin their silken snares between bushes and trees. While pushing my way through the woods at night I often feel their silken webs brush against my face and imagine that the spider has jumped off and is crawling about over my person. As a biolo-

The body form of the Nephila *spider is unusual, as are the tufts on its legs. It is the only spider that spins gold-colored silk.*

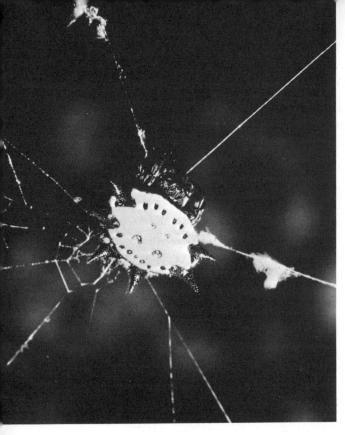

Another common orb-weaving spider in the vicinity of the lake is the star-bellied spider (Gasteracantha), characterized by its spiny abdomen and golden coloration. Tufts of silk are always attached to its web

Right: *Least expected of The Island's spiders is the trap-door spider that lives in a silk-lined tunnel beneath the ground. The entrance is closed by a hinged lid that is well camouflaged to match the surrounding area.*

gist, I am ashamed to admit that I have an instinctive fear of spiders; I am interested in spiders and their habits and realize that they are fascinating creatures, yet I have a deep-seated aversion to them, one that I share with many people. Any spider studies I make are carried out during the daylight hours when I can see where they are.

Another unusual spider on The Island is the star-bellied spider, *Gasteracantha*. The abdomens of these black and yellow spiders are shaped like five-pointed stars. They build their webs in wheel-like form but with the hubs open. At various points on the webs are attached bits of silken tufts, believed by some to act as lures to attract midge-eating insects. I often encounter the webs of these spiders in the island woodlands, especially across trails where night-flying insects are apt to abound.

A year or so ago, I discarded a large piece of cardboard along the path I usually follow when going to the blind at the cypress

lake. This morning as I passed by, I decided to examine the partially decomposed cardboard to see what creatures, if any, had sought refuge beneath it. In turning the soggy piece over I noticed that, at one point, it appeared to be attached to the ground. Invesigating, I found to my surprise that a trap-door spider had built its tunnel down through the cardboard and into the soil. The lid, or trap door, was located on the top of the board while the silk-lined tunnel extended about six inches into the soil below it. Previously I had never encountered these spiders on The Island and so decided to excavate the earth in order to expose the complete tunnel and, if possible, to capture the inmate.

With my machete I cut away the soft loam and eventually was able to lift out a section containing the tunnel and the spider inside. When placed in a glass container aboard the houseboat, the spider obligingly emerged and captured crickets dropped nearby. This, of course, afforded opportunity for making photographs.

There are a number of different kinds of trap-door spiders found

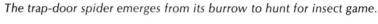

The trap-door spider emerges from its burrow to hunt for insect game.

in various parts of the United States and their habits vary to some extent. As their name indicates, the tunnels they make in the ground are closed with neatly fitting doors that are hinged with silk at one side. While inside, the spider holds the lid shut, making it quite difficult for an enemy to open it from the outside. To the outer surface of this trap door, the ingenious spider attaches camouflaging material to match the surroundings. If the nest is in an area covered with lichens, the lid will be covered with bits of lichen. In the case of the nest I excavated on The Island, the cardboard had been almost completely covered with fallen pine needles; the spider had attached these to the lid making it almost impossible to see. As a matter of fact, I suspect that trap-door spiders are much more common on The Island than might be suspected but, because of their effective method of camouflage, are not seen. In the case of the one I did find, it was only through its accidental location in the cardboard that it came to my attention.

Spiders appear to have singled out insects as their prey; almost all spiders confine their diets to them with but few exceptions. Among those that prefer other food is a spider, *Diapontia*, in Argentina that catches tadpoles, a spider in Africa, *Palystes*, that captures small lizards and snakes, while the large bird-eating spider, *Mygale*, of South America captures and devours birds.

One afternoon, while walking along the edge of the lake, I was astonished to find a small snake entangled in a spider web near the ground. The silken web was attached to a palmetto frond and the luckless snake was suspended in the web about three inches above the ground. I do not believe that the snake had accidentally become entangled in the web since the spider appeared to be shrouding it with layer after layer of silk and the snake was nearly dead. At this point I left, intending to obtain a camera to record the incident but, unfortunately, I never got back that day and so do not know whether or not the snake was actually fed on by the spider. Neither do I know the name of the spider. However, I later discovered that others, too, had seen similar occurrences. Henry McCook, writing in 1889, stated that a gentleman in Batavia, New York, "found in his wine cellar, a live striped snake, nine inches long, suspended between two shelves by the tail, by a spider's web. . . . In this situation the suffering snake hung, alive and furnished a continued feast for several large spiders [for several days]. The snake was eventually killed." It was thought that the spiders involved were *Tegenaria*, a type often found in cellars and neglected buildings. Other similar reported cases apparently involved spiders of the genus *Theridion*, often seen in and around houses. There have also been reliable reports of mice being entrapped in the webs of spiders.

Along the weedy margins of the cypress lake are found water spiders, *Dolomedes*, which rest upon the water's surface or on aquatic plants. These spiders often reach large size; I have seen individuals that measured up to two inches across their outstretched legs. When alarmed, they run rapidly away over the water, after the manner of water striders, or dive beneath the surface.

I am aware that these aquatic spiders sometimes capture and devour small fish and minnows, but I have never been fortunate enough to catch them in the act. It is reported that *Dolomedes* spiders sometimes destroy fish in hatcheries, especially small catfish up to as much as two inches in length. One of these spiders was seen capturing a top minnow, *Gambusia*, at Natchitoches, Louisiana.

It is apparent that spiders of some kinds have deviated from their usual insectivorous habits, and since the aquatic or "fishing" spiders are common around the lake I still have hopes that some quiet afternoon I shall be fortunate enough to see one in the act of capturing a minnow.

Chapter 8

THE RAINS COME

THE ISLAND FOREST has two distinct moods; in summer when the sun pours its warmth down through the trees and when the songs of the crickets and cicadas fill the air, it is a happy place, but when the rains come the forest takes on a more somber air, one that is, nonetheless, attractive. Falling rain drips from the pointed tips of the leaves and soaks into the ground, and most sounds disappear except for the voices of tree frogs and cricket frogs that echo discordantly across The Island from hidden retreats, always an accompaniment of the falling rain. During sunny days when the heat drifts like waves across The Island, the tree frogs nestle quietly among the epiphytic ferns and mosses or in tree cavities, conserving the moisture within their bodies. But the rains, slowly falling upon the forest, increase the humidity and moisten their naked skins, bringing body comfort. Then, like birds in spring, they sing their songs of peace and contentment since a sense of well-being, whether in man or frog, is happiness in its basic form. The tree frogs, soaking up the moisture from the falling rain, are revived and refreshed and feel again the ancient urge of self-expression. They expand their throats into balloon-like membranes which function like resonance chambers, causing their voices to carry far across the misty land.

Salamanders, too, hidden beneath rotting logs through the hot, dry days, are soon aware of the rain, stir their slime-covered bodies and emerge to crawl over the forest floor in search of food and

153

Mushrooms and other fungi push up out of the ground, and toads and frogs emerge from hidden places to enjoy the wetness.

During damp weather, snails emerge from coiled shells and move slowly over the vegetation, their stalked eyes extended.

Below: *During rainy weather, buzzards sit disconsolately in the trees, silhouetted against the sky.*

mates. Snails, long sealed within their coiled fortresses, extend soft bodies and explore their vicinities with stalked eyes; assured that all is well, they creep across the mossy carpets, leaving glistening slime trails behind them. Thus, during the period of rain, do the island's moisture-loving creatures come out from hidden refuges and take up active life again. While moisture falls they feed and mate but retire again into obscurity when the rains have gone, following an ever-recurring cycle.

On dead snags high overhead black vultures sit disconsolately as the rain falls upon their naked, repulsive heads and dark body feathers. But they are not asleep; their sharp eyes continually scan the damp forest spreading away below their perch. They note the marsh rabbit huddled upon a stump and follow a muskrat as it swims slowly across a woodland pool. But their observation of the living creatures below is only casual; they are not interested in living things.

The rain began falling before dawn this morning and now trickles in small rivulets down the trunks of the trees, wetting the mosses and ferns and contributing life-giving moisture to the strands of Spanish moss that hang from the limbs. The cells of the mosses imbibe the water and store it in special compartments against the certain drought. Their "leaves" uncurl and turn green and their chlorophyll once again begins manufacturing starch, using the feeble light filtering down from the leaden sky. During dry weather, when hot winds sear the ground and rattle the palmetto fronds harshly against each other, the resurrection ferns growing upon the great horizontal limbs of the live oaks curl up their leaves to conserve water. But, when the rains come, they unfold and change to brighter green and growth commences again. On the sides of dead stumps, now moistened by the water, the spores of other ferns germinate, producing green, heart-shaped gametophytes which, in time, will give rise to tiny fern plants and eventually spores, to continue the ancient cycle of fern life.

I am always surprised at the great change in color brought about in lichens by rain, whether it be the warm rain of summer or the

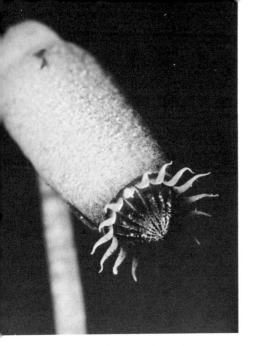

Left: *During dry weather, the spore-capsule teeth of mosses are spread open to allow the dust-like spores to escape.* Right: *With the coming of wet weather the teeth are closed.*

cold, dreary rain of autumn and winter. Today I notice that the lichens spreading over the trunks and limbs of the trees are vivid green and stand out in bold relief against the dark, wet bark. Before the rain, these same lichens were gray-green and inconspicuous, since the background of bark was gray or brownish. Having absorbed moisture, the lichens changed color and their slow growth has commenced again. Some Arctic lichens are among the slowest growing of all plants; but an inch in diameter, they are estimated to be a thousand years old.

I scrape away a portion of a crustose lichen from the trunk of a hornbeam and examine it under my hand lens, but under the low magnification I see only a mass of greenish tissue. I know, however, that if I were to study this lichen fragment under a microscope I would see green, spherical cells and, attached to them, transparent strands. This microscopic structure of lichens was for long a mystery to botanists; there seemed to be two different kinds of plant cells involved, yet the lichen behaved as one. Then it was discovered that a lichen is actually made up of two entirely different plants, a green alga and a fungus. The green, spherical algal cells manufacture food with the help of the sunlight, while the fungus encloses them and supplies them with nutritive materials and moisture. It is a remarkable cooperative arrangement and what is even more amazing is that these composite plants grow and reproduce as if they were one plant having its own characteristic style of growth. The problem that was dropped in the botanists' laps was this: Should they give each lichen a technical name, or should the fungus and the alga that compose each one have individual names? At present, each kind of lichen has its own name, but the matter is still not settled to everyone's satisfaction. At any rate, lichens are found everywhere, almost from pole to pole. Here on my island they are abundant, both in numbers and kinds.

Such are my thoughts as I walk across The Island in the soft summer rain while damp mists float out of the surrounding marshland and drift through the trees, sometimes hiding the more distant vistas behind slowly shifting films of opalescent fog. This creeping mist floats over the lake at The Island's center, blanketing its surface so that it no longer mirrors the surrounding trees. Now and again, passing showers sweep across the water like filmy curtains; the falling raindrops patter over the surface like tiny feet. Beyond the lake rise the towering trunks of more distant trees standing knee-deep in cottony fog and, seemingly, supported by nothing tangible. The great river beside The Island has disappeared, completely hidden by the nebulous fog, and beyond the shore there is nothing. It is here that my world comes to an abrupt end; my mind tells me that beyond the river there stretches another shore but it is only in my mind; my eyes are veiled by the mist and even the sounds of the flowing river are muffled.

Rain and mist are such common things that few of us ever give them much thought; we take them for granted as familiar parts of the world we live in. But look at this droplet of water hanging like a gleaming jewel from the tip of a cluster of pine needles. As I watch it, the drop becomes larger and larger as water flows down the tree and out onto the needles. When the droplet becomes so

Drops of moisture hang suspended from leaves and pine needles where they gleam like living jewels.

large that the cohesive forces holding it into spherical form are counterbalanced by its weight, it falls to the ground. Then another droplet begins forming and the process is repeated over and over as long as the rain continues to fall on the tree. But just where did this rain water come from and where has it been? Days, or perhaps weeks ago, this same water was probably in the Gulf. Associated with its molecules were the molecules of various salts and organic substances, the latter having originated from the living things of the sea. But the heat of the sun evaporated or distilled the water from the surface and its molecules were lifted upward and carried away to form clouds that floated inland over the land and the coastal marshes where the vapor coalesced into droplets that fell as rain. Having fallen from the sky, this same water flowed into the Gulf and the cycle began again. It is a cycle as old as the earth and this same water, evaporating and falling again and again, has refreshed plants and animals since the earth's most ancient days. Consider these droplets trembling here on the pine needles; they once fell upon the earth's hot rocks and were quickly turned into steam. But slowly the rocks were cooled by the caressing water that fell from the sky and eventually found its way to the sea. In this great caldron of water mixed with minerals leached out of the rocks, came life by some process that we as yet do not understand and perhaps never will.

Water was the essential part of this primordial witch's brew that gave birth to life and, once started, living things of endless variety emerged from the sea and spread over the barren rocks and eventually clothed the land with green vegetation through which animal life roamed. The droplets of water that fall on The Island this morning could tell an interesting story; some of their molecules may have flowed in the veins of ancient dinosaurs or up through the trunks of tree ferns in Carboniferous forests; they may have been frozen into ice on the polar ice caps or flowed down jungle streams in tropical Africa. The water in your morning coffee has been distilled and redistilled a million-million times. Water does not wear out or change; it is one of the most stable of all substances and, without it, life as we know it could not exist. It is the essential ingredient of every living thing from a virus to an elephant.

It is difficult to realize, as I walk through this island forest, what enormous amounts of water are being released into the air. If this water were emerging from the leaves as drops rather than as invisible vapor, it would be raining every day in the forest. Fortunately or unfortunately, depending on your attitude toward rain, the moisture that enters the air from living plants rises as vapor, eventually to form clouds. When conditions are right, this cloud-held moisture will fall as rain, bathing the leaves and washing them free of dust. The moisture revives the forest again and life goes on, always governed by the presence or absence of this remarkable compound we call water.

The effects of summer rains on The Island are as different from those of the cold rains of autumn and winter as daylight is from darkness. Summer rains awaken seeds that for long have lain dormant upon the dry ground; they stimulate the thread-like mycelia of fungi creeping through the soil and rotting logs. The fungi produce strange and often colorful mushrooms and fruiting bodies

Droplets of moisture collect on spider webs, weighting them down and making them resemble strings of glass beads.

that appear overnight as if by magic. All the moisture-loving things are awakened by the combination of warmth and life-giving moisture and they flourish for a time until the water has drained away or evaporated into the air. Winter rains, by contrast, are cold and cheerless and fall upon dead leaves littering the forest floor, hastening their decay and speeding up their return to humus. The tree frogs, safely hibernating within rotting logs or in hollow trees, no longer raise their voices; the living processes within their cold bodies have slowed down nearly to the death point and they are unaware of the passing winter; they know only the warm rains of spring and summer. Of all the amphibious clan, only the small cricket frogs remain active; they inhabit the grassy margins of the woodland pools, often raising their voices during damp winter nights.

Summer rain has a restorative quality, energizing the natural forces of growth. Today the rain has continued to fall and the forest and The Island are now saturated. The Spanish moss, draped from every available limb, has become filled with moisture and changed in color from gray to green. The falling rain picks up dust and organic matter from the limbs and leaves of the trees and carries it down, depositing it upon the Spanish moss, thus supplying it with needed minerals. This so-called moss is an air plant, but it does not subsist on air alone; it cannot live without nutrients washed down from the trees above. Strangest, perhaps, of all the local forms of plant life, it is actually a member of the pineapple family and native to the lands surrounding the Gulf of Mexico. Farther south, in Florida, forest trees are hosts to bromeliads, also air plants, which grow in the form of leaf rosettes containing pools of water in their bases. This water, collected during rainy periods, supplies the plants during drought. Within these arboreal leaf tanks live mosquito larvae and even dragonfly nymphs. But Spanish moss is on its own and has no such adaptation for storing water; it must absorb and hold the water it needs from the humid air and from falling rain. During much of the year, the Spanish moss on The Island is bathed in fog and thrives, seemingly, upon nothing. But this is an illusion because no plant can live without obtaining mineral elements and water from some source. Like the more usual plants that live upon the ground, it has, through long evolution, perfected and refined its way of life. Removed from competition with other plants, it grows abundantly wherever it can obtain sufficient moisture. Sometimes, a large oak may support several hundred pounds of this strange "moss" which is in no sense parasitic and apparently does no harm to the trees that harbor it.

As I pick my way gingerly through the spiny smilax vines near the fog-blanketed lake I encounter a large decaying log, now well saturated with water. Sections of the once-firm wood and bark have fallen away exposing creeping slime molds and other fungi that spread their gelatinous growths over the surface. My attention is attracted by a yellowish slime mold and I kneel down to examine it more closely. It consists of a fan-shaped mass of naked protoplasm with vein-like strands. I can see no movement, yet I know that it is creeping slowly along like a giant amoeba, engulfing and digesting, in its primitive way, food particles encountered on the moist wood over which it moves. The damp weather has brought it out of hiding from the deep crevices of the log through which it flowed like thick molasses. Slime molds are something of a paradox to biologists. Not too long ago, these lowly forms of life were considered to be animals and given the technical name *Mycetozoa*, meaning "fungus animal." More recently, as their biology has become better

After the rains have gone, slime molds creep over rotting logs, eventually transforming themselves into spore-bearing stalks of endless form.

understood, their classification has been revised and they are now considered to be a form of fungus called a *Myxomycete*, a term meaning "slime fungus." Still, it makes little difference to a slime mold whether we class it as a plant or an animal for it, like many other primitive living things, has not yet advanced down the evolutionary road to the place where the path divides, one way leading to the animal kingdom and the other to the plant kingdom. Down the slow eons it has followed its unobtrusive way, changing little but surviving in a world that has changed continuously.

As the glistening droplets of water fall from the damp trees around me I continue to watch the yellow slime mold. I know that if I mark the point where its leading edge moves along and observe it again an hour later, I shall find it to have advanced a fraction of an inch. I know, too, that when the rain has gone and the rotting wood has begun to dry, the slime mold will probably cease its movement over the log and form yellow clumps. In time, these will transform themselves into exquisite, spore-bearing structures called sporangia. A fraction of an inch tall, slime mold sporangia are of infinite variety. The one before me will produce tiny cones filled with what looks like orange cotton candy; others will transform into feather-like plumes, and yet others into intricate "birdcages" suspended from stands.

Pulling away another section of the bark from the fallen tree, I expose several other slime molds; some are creamy white while others have a golden hue. Most of these, I know, are not mature since they are of small size. These "young" slime molds will creep slowly into the deeper interstices of the soft wood when the sun returns to drive the dampness away.

A hundred feet or so beyond the rotting log stands a large stump seen vaguely through the dense vegetation. Long ago a logging crew apparently sawed down the tree, leaving a flat-topped stump. Suddenly my eyes are attracted by a large splotch of brilliant scarlet on its top and my first thought is that some wounded animal has shed considerable blood. I push through the vines and a closer look seems to confirm my first belief that the red material is, indeed, blood. I touch it cautiously with my finger and find that it is fluid in nature and certainly looks like freshly congealed blood. But where could it have come from? I look around on the opposite side of the stump and am surprised to see more "blood," but I notice that some of this has turned brown and that the surfaces of the splotches are raised in clumps. It now dawns on me that this is a slime mold of a type I have never observed before. I have come upon strange fungi in various hues but never before a bright scarlet one. The moral here, I suppose, is never to be surprised at things encountered in the woods. I have roamed these and other forests at all seasons and during almost every conceivable kind of weather, yet this is the first time I have ever seen this fungus. Why, I wonder, did it appear at this particular time and place? This question is very difficult to answer; evidently the stump is now at a favorable stage of its decay and moisture conditions are right for its development. Then, of course, chance plays a part. It has often been my experience as a biologist that when something unusual is found, another specimen is apt to show up very soon. For many years I looked for Indian pipes, and since discovering a clump of them here on The Island I have seen additional specimens several times. Perhaps this is because, having once seen them, my eyes became conditioned to their appearance, making it easier to notice them again. Will this be true, I wonder, of the scarlet slime mold?

And so I leave the multicolored slime molds flowing imperceptibly over the logs and stumps and walk away along the margin of the lake, conscious that I am surrounded by living things of infinite variety, but aware, also, that my presence has had no effect upon their destined ways. I have an acute consciousness of the living world around me; they do not.

Anyone who roams or fishes in the river bottoms and bayous of the Deep South is bound eventually to hear tales of the congo eel, a slimy creature with tiny legs and, supposedly, a deadly bite. Often hooked by fishermen, these eels are seldom encountered anywhere except in sluggish water, so I am very much surprised, on this rainy morning, to discover a specimen coiled up beneath a section of bark that has fallen from a dead snag. At first I think I have uncovered a snake since it gives vent to a loud hissing sound, causing me to recoil quickly. After recovering my composure, I approach and am surprised to find that it is a congo eel, a female coiled around a

Congo eels (Amphiuma) *crawl out of the water during autumn rains and deposit their strings of grape-like eggs in rotten stumps. When the eggs hatch, the gill-bearing young return to the water to complete their development.*

mass of eggs. The eggs are the size of small grapes, all connected to one another like a string of beads. Gingerly I lift the eggs with a stick in order to examine them closely. As I do so, the female attempts to bite me and since the jaws of these animals are armed with needle-like teeth that can inflict ugly gashes which are often slow to heal, I treat her with respect.

I wish to examine the congo eel's eggs aboard the houseboat so I place them in a collecting bag. When seen later under a lens, it was obvious that they were about to hatch since the active young could be seen through the thin, transparent membranes enclosing them. Within twenty-four hours they all hatch and I discover that each one has a pair of feather-like gills, a condition not found in the adults. When released in the river, they swim rapidly away, apparently quite capable of caring for themselves.

These creatures are not eels at all but a type of large mud puppy or salamander, known scientifically as *Amphiuma*. There are two kinds, but local fishermen make no distinction between them. One type has two toes on its feet while the other has three toes. What confuses the public mind is that they are quite eel-like and slimy. They have legs but these are so reduced in size as to be almost useless for crawling. Here, no doubt, is a case where legs are slowly being lost by disuse through the slow processes of evolution. Given a few million years more, congo eels will probably be legless. Contrary to local opinion, these animals are not poisonous.

They are known by colloquial names, including ditch eel, deaf adder, and lamper eel. Sometimes they are called congo snakes as well as congo eels. Where "congo" enters the picture is a mystery; perhaps it is because they do appear to be something that might have come out of Africa. It is possible that the name comes from conger eel, a true eel found in the sea. The latter animal is not related to the congo eel, which is a type of salamander. In any case, they are native animals that feed upon crayfish, earthworms, and clams. Not much is really known about the breeding habits of these large salamanders, but, apparently, when ready to lay her mass of eggs the female leaves the water, probably during a wet spell, and finds a suitable place to hide. Here she deposits her eggs and settles down to guard them. She may remain with them for an extended period, but when rains come again, the young burst out of their membranes and crawl away toward the nearest water. In time they lose their gills and grow into adults that may often reach nearly a yard in length. On The Island, the spot where I located the eel's nest was but a few feet from the lake so the young would have no trouble in finding water and it was probably out of the lake that the gravid female had originally come.

On this trip to The Island my stay was extended for some days and I had opportunity to note the delayed effects of the rains. There had been a period of drought and seeds had fallen upon the ground and remained there, their living embryos quiescent within protective seed coats. Seed-eating birds had, of course, consumed many of them but, with the coming of rain, the latent life was stimulated into growth. Small tussocks of green grass sprang up in some places and in others the tiny leaves of flowering plants pushed up out of the soil. Many seeds, I know, were not stimulated into germination by the brief period of moisture; they needed a ripening period, or even winter's cold, to bring about their germination.

Watching how the plant life of The Island was aroused by the short period of rain, I was strongly reminded of the arrival of rainy seasons in the Tropics. During the dry season, humidity is low and seeds that fall from jungle trees and vines lie upon the ground. There are few blooms. Then, almost overnight, the rains arrive and life takes up again its period of active growth and fructification. Roads into the back country that for months have been dusty now soak up the rain and are transformed into morasses where only the carabao can plod its leisurely way. Vines spring out of the black soil in the half light of the jungle and snake up the trees as if in a great hurry to reach the sun. It is a time of active growth. There is really not much difference between a truly tropical island and my island. Here, as in the Tropics, lianas anchor themselves to the trees, seeking support for their struggle upward toward the stronger light. Only the kinds of lianas are different; their manner of growth is

The berry-like fruit of the wax myrtle (Myrica) is covered with wax.

the same. Here, also, there are two seasons; there is the summer with its warm intermittent rain and heat, and the winter with its more abundant rain and cold temperature. In the Tropics, there is the dry season when growth is slowed down, not by low temperature but by deficient water; then comes the rainy season when plant life flourishes once more. In one place the governing factor is temperature; in the other, it is the presence or absence of moisture.

And so here on my island, I watch with interest the after-effects of the summer rain. The second day after the skies cleared, I set out to walk across The Island. Circling a pool of water and pushing my way through the dense growths of palmetto and fern, I come abruptly out into a glade surrounded by low wax myrtle bushes. I have visited this spot many times before but on this morning I am astonished to see the ground covered with beautiful specimens of poisonous amanita mushrooms, identified by their cup-like bases and the rings or veils around their stems. One kind, the destroying angel, is snow-white while the other, the fly amanita, has an orange cap covered with scales. Both kinds are highly poisonous. The fly amanita received its name because its poison is so powerful that flies feeding upon its viscid juice are often killed in large numbers.

Of all the common mushrooms encountered on The Island the amanitas are probably the most attractive; but beautiful things are often deadly and no better example could be found to illustrate this point than these fungi. The deadly fly amanita, *Amanita muscaria,* thrusting its golden cap above the dark leaf-litter beside the trail, is very lovely; its form is graceful and its coloration runs through shades of gold and pale yellow. It is a thing of beauty but its tissues contain muscarin, a deadly poison that can quickly kill a person. Ten feet away is another amanita, *Amanita phalloides*, known as the destroying angel. Its whiteness stands out in striking contrast against the dark forest floor. But, like its relative, the fly amanita, it is as deadly as it is beautiful. On the other hand, Caesar's amanita, *Amanita caesarea*, is not believed to be poisonous, in contrast to the other members of the group. Of all the amanitas, this is the most attractive of all, to me. Its brilliant red cap pushes up out of the ground surrounded by the white tissues of the cup. When fully expanded, the cap is scarlet at the center, shading away to bright

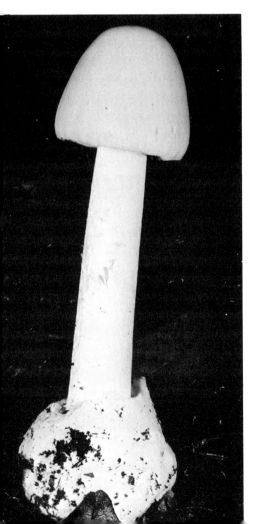

Left: Amanita *mushrooms push up from the forest floor. Snow-white and attractive, their flesh is deadly. Below: Delicate cup fungi, golden in color, grow among green mosses on fallen logs.*

yellow near the margins. When a group of these mushrooms is seen growing on the ground the sight is both startling and spectacular. On several occasions I have come upon them on The Island and always my reaction has been one of astonishment and pleasure at seeing objects of such loveliness and I am amazed that the black humus can produce such beautiful fungi. This mushroom, history tells us, constituted the last meal of the Roman Emperor, Claudius Caesar. His death did not result from the mushrooms but from poison added to them. Yet, it is from this ancient incident that the attractive mushroom derived its name.

Natives in certain areas of Siberia often prepare concoctions of amanita mushrooms and drink them, the brew apparently inducing strange hallucinations and sensations, perhaps akin to those resulting from the taking of certain narcotic drugs. Why the participants in these weird orgies are not killed outright is a mystery; perhaps it is because the toxic material, muscarin, is excreted very rapidly by the kidneys. In any event, this form of "Russian roulette" is definitely not recommended to those seeking a thrill.

Many of the most beautiful plants (and some animals) have deadly qualities and use beauty and color to advertise their dangerous natures. This is, of course, a matter of self-protection; there is little to be gained by a plant or an animal being poisonous if it is unknowingly eaten. The poisonous plant or animal has had its revenge but it is a belated revenge that has served no useful purpose. To gain any advantage, potential enemies must be warned in some way. I do not have far to look for a good example to illustrate this point; here on this leaf is a very handsome caterpillar moving its head from side to side as it feeds. It is hardly an inch long and green in color with a bright orange spot on its back. Attached to the fore and hind portions of its body are needle-like spines. It is striking in appearance and if I did not know better I would probably pick up this innocent-looking little creature in order to examine it more closely. But, fortunately, for both myself and the caterpillar, I am warned by its distinctive coloration that it is a saddleback, *Sibine stimulea*, one of the most poisonous of all insects. If I were to pick it up in my fingers, the venom contained in the needle-like spines would enter my hand and, it is possible, or even probable, that I would need medical attention within a few minutes. I learned this from past experience and I will not soon forget. This same principle applies to the rattlesnake that warns an intruder before it is stepped upon.

Perhaps, of course, the amanita mushrooms are not good examples of warning coloration because some kinds are not distinctively colored or marked. Evidently, however, they have a warning odor since I have noticed that these mushrooms are never fed upon by gray squirrels in places where almost every nonpoisonous kind is eaten with avidity.

While the amanitas are almost all deadly if eaten, there seems to be some question as to the poisonous nature of the royal agaric or Caesar's amanita; some authorities hedge by saying that while not poisonous, they should not be eaten. Personally, I'm not going to experiment; I'm afraid of almost all wild mushrooms. Over there beside that palmetto is a group of very attractive parasol mushrooms *(Lepiota)*. Around their stems, just below the scaly caps, each one has a ring or collar and the base of its stem is bulbous. Both of these characteristics fit the deadly amanitas. Authorities on fungi state that there is no poisonous species with which the edible mushroom can be confused. This may be true and I am sure that if I had more confidence in my ability as an amateur mycologist I might try eating them. Still, they resemble the amanitas far too closely for comfort and I'm taking no chances.

Mushrooms are a form of plant life that appears overnight, seemingly out of nowhere. Several days ago I passed this way and saw not a single one; their creeping mycelia were still hidden beneath the soil, awaiting only the arrival of rain to stimulate the formation of the spore-bearing mushrooms that would push upward above the ground where their reproductive spores could be liberated and carried away by the wind. Here before me, the royal agarics spread across the forest floor, their scarlet color in striking contrast to the somber earth. Freshly emerged, their caps are lovely

During damp weather, delicate fairy mushrooms (Mycena) *thrive on rotten logs.*

but I know they cannot long remain so in the hot summer sun. By tomorrow they will have shriveled and their gaudy colors faded. Insects of many kinds will tunnel through their tissues, eventually destroying them completely.

So attractive and eye-catching are the royal agarics that I fail, at first, to notice other, smaller, mushrooms growing in the immediate vicinity. Here on a dead leaf is a cluster of tiny, delicate mushrooms with rust-red caps and slender, black stems. They are known as bell-shaped marasmius mushrooms. Their caps are barely a quarter inch in diameter and they receive their sustenance from the decaying tissues of the dead leaf upon which they grow. Beautifully formed and delicate as thin tissue, they appear only during periods of wet weather and last but a brief time, only long enough to shed their microscopic spores.

Having discovered these mushrooms, I realize that this is the time

to see what other types of fungi have appeared, so I walk on across
The Island in the warm morning sun. The dew is rapidly disappear-
ing and some interesting and delicate fungi may not long remain
attractive, especially if they are exposed to the direct sun. Fungi
are plants of the night.

Some of the most unusual kinds, I know, grow upon fallen trees
and rotting wood so I concentrate my search in such places and am
soon rewarded by finding several other types. One of these is a
coral fungus, *Clavaria*, which actually resembles a branch of beautiful, snowy coral growing upward out of rotting wood. It looks
far too pretty to eat but is said to be edible. On a nearby log is another type of coral mushroom, *Sparassis*, pale yellow in color with
its spore-bearing surfaces curled against each other so as to form a
more or less globular head. It, also, is supposed to be edible.

Another log a short distance away is almost completely covered
with bracket fungi of semicircular form. Each one is about three
inches in diameter and brownish in color with white edges. When

The bright yellow forms of
coral fungi (Clavaria) *push up*
through the mossy carpets.

I examine them closely I notice that each individual fungus is marked by numerous rings which, no doubt, have resulted from spurts of fresh growth stimulated by successive summer rains. These common fungi not only occur upon fallen logs but are often seen on dead, standing tree trunks. This particular one is *Polyporus versicolor*, but there are numerous other kinds, all of which grow on dead wood.

On this ramble through the woods today I have kept a sharp lookout for the bear's-head hydnum, one of the most amazing and beautiful of all the dead-wood fungi. Previously I have seen this fungus only once; it was growing on the side of a dead snag that leaned far out over the Pascagoula River in such a position that it was impossible to photograph it. It was during a cool spell in late autumn when rains had been falling for several days. Needless to say, I was most disappointed as I passed by in a boat and could view this attractive fungus only from a distance. It was snow-white in color, a foot across, and made up of teeth or spines all pointing downward like slender icicles. It was easy to see why it is called bear's-head hydnum since it did look a little like a shaggy animal's head—an albino, perhaps. The hydnums are tooth fungi and there are a number of different kinds; this one was *Hydnum caput-ursi*. I still have hopes that someday I shall see another specimen, one located where I can photograph it.

On some excursions in the woods one finds little of interest; on other days something worth looking at appears at every turn. Happily, today is one of those times when there seems to be something to see almost everywhere. Near the northern shore of The Island I come upon an open glade where I again find ideal conditions for mushroom growth. During a past hurricane, numerous trees have been felled and these dead trees are now in the proper state of decomposition to encourage abundant fungus growth. Wood-rot fungi of many kinds are present, many of which are quite colorful. On the ground, also, there are unusual mushrooms, including such kinds as the indigo lactarius and the orange bolete. The former is an unusual mushroom since it is deep purple in color and has bright purple juice. It is supposed to be edible but the coloration alone would make me hesitate. Nearby, there are several specimens of bolete mushrooms, *Boletus*, with large orange caps and yellow undersurfaces. I pull one up and turn it over, noting that, instead of radiating gills as in most mushrooms, its undersurface is covered with thousands of minute pores. This characteristic identifies it as a pore mushroom and it is within the pores that the reproductive spores are produced.

Returning across The Island toward the houseboat by a well-marked trail that I have followed many times, I pause to rest on a convenient stump. The sun is now high overhead and many birds are singing in the surrounding woods. Above me in a hornbeam tree, a flycatcher sits on a limb, occasionally darting away to snap up flying insects. I can distinctly hear the click of its beak. Soon I become aware of a most disagreeable odor and thinking that perhaps some wild animal has voided its excrement in the vicinity, I examine the ground nearby. I see no such evidence and have about decided that my nose has played me false when I notice a dark gelatinous mass on the ground about six feet away. This seems worth investigating so I go over to take a look and discover it to be a clump of stinkhorn fungi *(Phallus impudicus)* having a most disgusting odor. I have seen this fungus but once before and recall that my reaction, then, was the same as at present.

While most mushrooms and mushroom-like fungi depend on winds to disperse their spores, the stinkhorns produce a sticky, odoriferous substance that attracts flies. In feeding on this evil-smelling material, the flies become covered with fungus spores and carry them away to new locations. The fungus uses insects for the dispersal of its spores in a manner quite similar to that used by flowers to entice insects to carry their pollen.

Some mushrooms are filled with fluid and quickly degenerate into a mass of decaying slime soon after they have shed their spores; others merely dry out while still retaining their original form and color. In most cases, a mushroom is quickly invaded by insects of various kinds that bore through its tissues, hastening its destruction.

there are numerous small beetles and flies—the latter of the family Mycetophilidae—that confine their feeding mostly to fungi. The name of this fly family means "fungus-loving." Certain mushrooms are fed upon more enthusiastically than others; some poisonous amanitas, as we have seen, are almost immune to insect attack. Another mushroom that seems to hold little attraction for insects is the golden chantarelle, *Cantharellus aurantiacus*, a yellow mushroom having its cap depressed at the center, giving it a crater-like form. I encountered a group of these along the way and stopped long enough to photograph them. Several days later I passed by them again and noticed that they were still in good condition despite the drying heat; the only change I could see was their somewhat faded coloration. The golden chantarelle was once believed to be poisonous but modern mycologists consider it edible in spite of its bitter taste. Somewhat similar in appearance are the jack-o'-lantern mushrooms which are bioluminescent; I once saw them during a night excursion on The Island.

During succeeding days, the hot summer sun passed overhead on its appointed round, shedding its heat upon The Island and the marshland. The vultures again circled effortlessly in the sky and the cicadas sounded their drums in monotonous bursts which reverberated through the forest, rising and falling in a regular rhythm. Snails upon the forest floor withdrew their soft bodies into spiral shells, sealing the entrances with mucus that hardened. Deep within fallen logs, the slime molds flowed slowly through the crevices, feeding in their primitive way and awaiting the coming of another rain. Large black carpenter ants emerged from nests in rotting wood and hunted for game among the fallen leaves while, high overhead, pileated woodpeckers hammered upon dead snags thrust upward against a sky barren of clouds. And so the hot summer days followed each other in a monotonous chain while forest and island and marshland settled down to a slow routine, punctuated only by the cool of the nights. Life-giving rains would fall again; in the meantime, The Island and its varied inhabitants patiently awaited the day.

Chapter 9

AN INCIDENT OF ALLIGATORS

TODAY, SHORTLY AFTER NOON, we arrived at The Island and maneuvered the houseboat into position alongside the large cypress to which it is usually made fast. From the boat's deck I could look deeply into the island forest where the warm spring sunshine slanted down upon the sandy soil near the shore and dappled the floor of the deeper forest with patterns of light and shadow that trembled as sultry breezes slowly swayed the trees. Overhead, ever-present vultures circled gracefully in the sky, their outspread wings seemingly motionless as their eyes surveyed the world below. Along the shore, fiddler crabs scurried here and there among the mud-stained stems of aquatic plants, and water striders ran over the water, their feet making tiny depressions in the elastic surface film. The Island and its inhabitants appeared normal, unchanged since my last visit.

When the boat's motors had ceased their throbbing sound, the sudden vacuum of silence become filled with the songs of woodland birds; catbirds and mockingbirds voiced their joy of living from nearby trees and from along the shore came the familiar, sibilant rustling of the marsh grasses in the moving current. My ears, dulled by the constant throb of the motors, were suddenly sensitized to the varied sounds of The Island and I thrilled to the soft whisperings of the river and to the rustling of the palmettos along the shore. Once again I had come home to my island, that bit of land so familiar yet always so new to me.

On the limb of a nearby hickory, a pair of skinks (Eumeces), *male and female, engage in courting behavior. The head of the male (left) is bright red. When young, these lizards have sky-blue tails.*

The tide was high, with the result that there would be some delay in rigging a gangplank to the shore. Impatiently I walked up and down the catwalk along the side of the houseboat, looking for signs of life in the trees and on the nearby shore which, barely ten feet distant, remained so inaccessible because of deep water. There was no choice but to await the falling of the tide in order to reach the solid ground of The Island so, in the meantime, I mounted my telescope on the top deck and scanned the forest and the river, searching for movement in the quiet scene. Through the lens, close-up details sprang sharply into focus; a chameleon dressed in vivid green crawled slowly up the trunk of a hornbeam, pausing now and then to expand its crimson throat pouch. Deeper in the forest, near a bayberry, small skinks darted about searching for insect game, their sky-blue tails dragging behind them.

Turning next to a dead snag, I sweep the telescope up the trunk past old woodpecker holes and pieces of dead bark. Under its magnification, all the details of the dead tree come into focus; there are cracks in the wood caused by shrinkage and tiny holes made by boring beetles. Suddenly there comes into view a *Thalessa* wasp in the act of drilling into the wood to deposit her egg in a grub deeply hidden within it. Clearly I can discern how her slender ovipositor is bent in a loop to enable it to penetrate at a right angle into the wood. The large wasp rests quietly, but I know that her stylet-like drill is slowly boring through the hard wood toward a hidden insect larva. How does she know that the larva is there and how has she established its exact location? I do not know; yet she drills toward it with great precision. When it is reached she will force an egg down through her slender egg tube and her larva will parasitize the unfortunate grub. I cannot see the hidden grub, yet I know that it is there because the *Thalessa* wasp does not waste her time in useless endeavor. She is like a tiny electronic device with reactions as accurate and predictable. The wasp survives because she is, in a sense, a precision instrument, her habits perfected by millions of years of evolution. She does not "know" that there is a grub within the wood; her senses in some fashion have focused upon the grub like a radar and she is stimulated to drill into the wood at a certain point and to deposit an egg. She is an unthinking instrument following an ancient and instinctive ritual, so vital to the survival of her race.

I could, of course, spend the entire afternoon watching the wasp as her slender ovipostor bores inward through the wood, but my time would be wasted since the real drama will occur when her instrument breaks into the hidden grub's tunnel where no eye can watch. Then, her egg-laying act completed, she will fly away to locate grubs in other dead trees and her work will start again.

And so I leave the *Thalessa* toiling in her destined way and sweep the lens across the river to the far shore where a row of cooter turtles basks on a log in the warm sun. Now and again one individual, less indolent than its fellows, raises its head, perhaps to watch for enemies, and I can see the glint of its eyes in the sunlight. Beyond the turtles there stretches a mud flat fringed by reeds and in their shadows I notice a muskrat sitting upright like a squirrel as it feeds upon an opened clam. Having consumed the clam and discarded the shell, the muskrat enters the water and swims about, eventually emerging with another clam. Usually we think of these

Seen through a telephoto lens, a large dragonfly perches on a twig above the lake. Now and again it darts away in pursuit of flying insects.

large rodents as being vegetarians but, like most wild creatures, they take whatever food they can find, vegetable or animal, as is proved by the empty clam shells strewn on mud flats near The Island, the remains of past muskrat meals.

I next move the probing eye of the 'scope upward and scan the distant trees, the cypresses and oaks, following their trunks and limbs where lichens and epiphytic ferns grow in profusion. Here and there are deep cavities, their dark entrances standing out in sharp contrast against the lighter bark. No doubt these are the homes of wild creatures—flying squirrels, perhaps—but I look in vain for signs of habitation.

Suddenly something flashes across the field of view and when I have focused the 'scope properly I find it to be a crested flycatcher. It perches quietly on a cypress limb extending out over the river, perhaps fifty feet above the surface. As I watch, the bird darts away in a circular path and returns to its perch. Again and again I see this same performance and I know that it is capturing flying insects but, because of the great distance, I am unable to see the tiny insect or the actual act of capture.

In my preoccupation with watching the forest and the river through the telescope I have lost track of time, but I now find that the tide has fallen sufficiently to allow the gangplank to be rigged. With this means of egress established, I step at last upon The Island and my feet make crunching sounds on the shifting sand. Following my usual habit after long absence I make my way along the southern shore where the demarkation between land and marsh is ill defined and the two situations merge one with the other. A dense growth of buttonbushes grows on the island's margin just beyond which stretches the vast marshland with its tall grasses and reeds arising from soft muck.

Progress along the shore is arduous; spiny smilax vines and other lianas block the way making detours necessary every few feet. Underfoot, the earth is soft and yielding and there are spots where my feet sink deeply into the mud. Some of these spots are treacherous, camouflaged by thin surface growths of mosses which actually offer no support.

Because of its inaccessibility, this part of The Island is seldom visited by other humans, so wild creatures live undisturbed; some marsh birds nest along the shore and I once discovered the nest of a black vulture in the end of a hollow log.

Having made my way through the depths of this jungle-like portion of the island I come to a more open area that is screened from the marshland by a dense growth of buttonbushes. Here, much to my surprise, rises a mound about two feet high and five feet in diameter consisting of decayed vegetable matter mixed with dead reeds and sticks. Its location is approximately twenty feet from the edge of the marsh and, at first, I am mystified as to its significance. There gradually dawns on me the realization that this mound is an alligator nest, the first I have ever seen except in pictures. My immediate inclination is to dig into it to make sure. However, I resist the temptation and reconnoiter the surroundings.

Between the mound and the marsh there is a path, recently used, I am sure, because it is wet as if a reptile had, but a short time previously, emerged from the water and passed over the trail. Where is she now? I wonder; perhaps she is watching me from among the dark recesses of the tall marsh plants. It is not a comfortable feeling, since I have no desire to face an angry alligator alone in a remote portion of this island. Normally alligators are not dangerous, but perhaps a nesting female could be vicious.

Finally I decide to retire to the safety of higher ground a hundred

feet inland and await developments. There are still several hours of daylight so I sit down on a log. The alligator will probably return to her nest and I can at least watch her; unfortunately I do not have a camera along.

I fear that the cow alligator—yes, the female is called a cow—will not appear while I am in the vicinity so my mind soon becomes preoccupied with other things. A catbird, disturbed by my presence, sets up a commotion in a titi tree and a thrasher scratches about among dead leaves in search of food—normal sounds of the forest. Beyond the marsh, the afternoon sun is now and then obscured by heavy clouds drifting slowly across the sky. I am alone between the worlds of marshland and forest and only in my memory is there a different world teeming with cities and people. Before me is a huge nest constructed by a gigantic reptile, a survivor from the ancient past long before there were men.

I do not know how long I am lost in reverie, but suddenly I am brought back to the present by a movement in the water's edge where the head of a large 'gator appears. For a minute or so it remains stationary, only its snout, eyes, and a portion of its back above the surface. Apparently it is surveying the scene. Assured that the coast is clear, the alligator emerges from the water and begins crawling slowly toward the nest. Exactly how long this cow is I have no way of knowing precisely, but she is certainly at least ten feet from snout to tip of tail.

In truth, she is an ugly and vicious-looking creature having angular jaws set with numerous teeth. Her neck is heavy, as if filled with fat or muscles, and along her back from neck to tail extend rows of keeled scales. She lumbers toward the nest and crawls upon it. Here she pauses and I am at a loss as to what she is doing. Gradually I become aware that she is voiding water from her anal opening upon the nest, apparently to moisten it. Other observers, I later found, have likewise noticed this act.

Beyond the bayou at the southern side of The Island lies alligator country, a watery waste where the large reptiles feed. The females nest along the shore in the foreground.

The female alligator watches her nest from the nearby bayou, her periscopic eyes alert for any intruder.

Reassured by the slow movements of the huge reptile, I decide to approach nearer, convinced that I can outrun her because of her short legs. Cautiously I walk out into the open, but the 'gator immediately senses my presence and swings around toward me, at the same time opening her great jaws to reveal the white interior of her mouth. She raises her heavy body from the nest and moves her tail from side to side and from her throat there issues a loud hissing sound. Her attitude is definitely threatening and, indeed, she certainly looks vicious, so I move no closer since I really do not know how fast she can run. My thoughts turn backward to a time in the western mountains when I inadvertently came between a mother bear and her cubs, nearly with disastrous results. I have no desire to test the extent of this alligator's mother instinct.

In that open glade along The Island's far shore I watch this great reptile as she gives every evidence of defending her nest by any force necessary. The day is dying and the light fading, adding an eerie feeling to the strange scene. Here is a man of the twentieth century facing a huge antediluvian beast; in fancy I am transported back in time to the days of the ancient reptiles.

Not especially in fear but in sober discretion, I withdraw from the scene, leaving the cow alligator in charge of her precious nest. It is nearly dark by the time I arrive at the houseboat.

Having discovered the secret nesting place of the alligators, I cannot rest until I return for more observations and, perhaps, pictures of these beasts in their natural habitat. Early next morning I again make my way across The Island and cautiously approach the open glade where the nest is located. The cow is nowhere in sight, but I have no doubt that she is nearby and I have no desire to give her any argument.

If there is one alligator nest in the vicinity it seems reasonable to assume that there may be others, so I continue walking on along the island's margin. Hardly a hundred yards farther, I am pleased to see another nest, this time, apparently, in the process of construction. There is a low mound of dead marsh grasses and a slick path over the mud leading out of the nearby bayou. Since the path shows evidence of recent use I assume that the 'gator has been actively working, so I retire behind a large cypress to wait. Shortly the cow appears and crawls upon the nest, but she apparently does not see me and remains but a short time. She then returns to the bayou but reappears after a few minutes, this time carrying a bundle of marsh grass in her mouth. She places it on the mound and crawls around and over the nest, apparently mashing it down. For some reason I find her act completely out of character; perhaps it is because it was somewhat paradoxical to see such a vicious-looking beast carrying a mouthful of grass! In any event, I watch for more than an hour as she returns again and again, each time carrying grass which she adds to the mound.

Farther along the shore, I locate yet another nest, this time a fully developed one, presumably containing eggs. It consists of a mound of vegetable matter about three feet high covered by a thin layer of dry mud, a feature designed probably to prevent the plant material from drying. Since the cow does not immediately show up to pro-

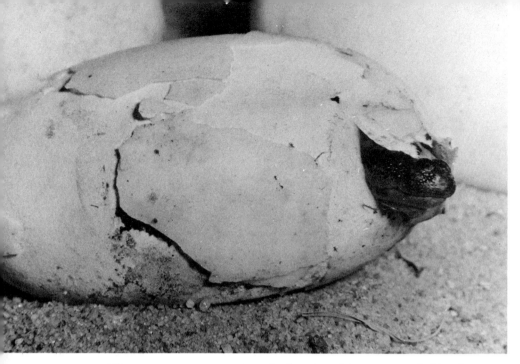

Alligator eggs are approximately the size of hen eggs and, like them, are covered with hard shells. When fully developed the young 'gator breaks out of the egg.

tect her nest, I decide to dig into it.

About six inches below the surface the first eggs are encountered. Since I have never seen alligator eggs I am very much interested in finding them covered with hard shells resembling those of the chicken. Vaguely I expected them to have rubbery shells like snake eggs. Each egg is about two and a half inches in length and one and a half inches in diameter—about the size of a hen's egg—and oval in shape.

All together, there are thirty-six eggs concentrated within the central portion of the nest mound and I notice that the temperature within the mound is perceptibly higher than that outside. Later, I discovered that E. A. McIlhenny of Louisiana had recorded the interior temperatures of many alligator nests and found that they averaged about twenty degrees Fahrenheit, higher than temperatures outside in the shade. In other words, temperatures within the nest averaged between 102° F. and 92° F. while outside night temperatures varied from 66° F. to 83° F. During the day, however, temperatures outside the nest reached about the same level as those recorded inside. The fact remains that the heat generated by the decaying vegetation tends to incubate the eggs. The decaying material, covered by a layer of mud, insulates the eggs from the cooler night temperatures with the result that temperatures within the nest remain almost constant, allowing the embryos within the eggs to develop. For the eggs to mature normally, the vegetation making up the nest must be kept moist; thus has arisen the cow's habit of voiding water over the nest periodically. Subsequently I examine several other nests, every one of which is moist, even though there has been no recent rain.

In the interest of scientific investigation, I decide to rob this nest of its eggs and to observe their hatching at home. I remove all thirty-six, along with a quantity of the plant material, and carry them

An alligator nest consists of decaying vegetable matter piled in a large heap. The eggs, buried inside, are incubated by the heat from the sun and the decaying vegetation.

Here are three alligator eggs, from one of which a young alligator is emerging.

Below: Young alligators are guarded by the female for some time after hatching. She calls them by means of grunting sounds.

back to the houseboat in a tub. Later, these were placed on my back porch at home and moistened periodically. I anxiously awaited results. Under normal conditions I found that alligator eggs require about two months to hatch but I have no means of knowing how long these have already been incubating. Like a foster mother, I tended the "alligator nest" on my porch, much to my wife's vexation.

Fortunately I did not have long to wait; within a week I heard little grunting noises emanating from the tub and upon examination of the eggs discovered that their shells were cracking. Within a few hours several small alligators had emerged measuring between eight and nine inches in length; they were bright-eyed and active. It was, perhaps, a tribute to me, their foster mother, that only one egg out of thirty-six failed to hatch.

The problem then was: what to do with thirty-five baby 'gators? Obviously I could not continue to keep them on my back porch if marital peace was to continue. My final decision was to liberate them some distance away in a lake owned by my family. The little 'gators were placed in the water near a wooded section of the shore where there were numerous willows. To me, it looked like an ideal place for alligators. They swam about in the water, seemingly reluctant to leave. I shooed them away but still they remained nearby and it occurred to me that perhaps they considered me to be their real mother since I was the only living thing that they had seen since hatching.

Under wild conditions, young alligators are guarded by the cow for some time, until they are about three feet long. They have many enemies; they are preyed upon by gars, 'coons, and even by adult 'gators. It is also probable that large water birds sometimes capture them.

I left the little group of baby 'gators in the lake, but as I walked away they all turned toward me as if accusing me of desertion. Each morning for a week or so I returned to the spot and each time saw no evidence of their presence until I had uttered an imitation of the mother alligator's call consisting of "umph-umph-umph." To be effective this grunting sound must be made in the throat with the mouth closed. Whenever I gave this alligator call, the baby alligators came swimming from all directions and congregated at my feet along the bank where I fed them bits of meat. This was a touching show of confidence in me as a foster mother but I eventually realized that, as wild creatures, they must learn to shift for themselves, so I deserted them. Whether or not any of my foster 'gators survived I have not yet discovered. This incident occurred several years ago and recently I found what was apparently an alligator egg shell washed up on a bank, so it is just possible that some of them at least have grown to mating and egg-laying size. I am quite sure that there were no alligators in the lake originally.

Until the coming of man the alligators of the bayous were masters of all they surveyed, but even now they do not fear man; they simply avoid him when possible. They feed upon crayfish, crabs, and fish and occasionally snatch waterfowl from below the surface. Sometimes they capture and devour swimming hogs or dogs and they are also prime enemies of the muskrats that inhabit the marsh. Fortunately, humans are not among their preferred food items, though a large 'gator could easily kill a man.

The alligator received its name from the Spanish *el largarto* meaning "the lizard," but it belongs to the crocodile family as does the true crocodile found in southern Florida and other places farther south. While the early Spanish-speaking people of Central and South America called these creatures "lizards," the settlers in the Gulf Coast region knew them as *crocodriles* (pronounced ko-ko-drees). In many South Louisiana parishes there are still lakes bearing the name Cocodrie, so called because alligators were abundant there. Before the coming of the Spanish and French settlers to this region, the native American Indians knew and hunted the alligators

With its head protruding from the egg, a young 'gator surveys the world. Part of the shell is at the right.

Completely out of the egg, this young alligator is about eight inches long.

for their flesh and skins. To the Biloxi Indians, they were known as *nuxwoti* and the places where they were abundant as *nuxoda-payixya*. The name *hachunchuba*, meaning "without hair," was applied to them by the local Choctaws, and "Chinchuba" towns, creeks, and bayous may still be found on maps of the region, the name being a phonetic derivation of the original Indian word.

On warm spring nights I have cruised the bayous in the vicinity of The Island, listening to the primeval *umph, umph, umph* calls uttered by the female alligators with young, and to the deeper bellows of the bulls. In the beam of my flashlight I have spotted their blood-red eyes among the reeds, eyes that quietly watched but did not move. The alligator is truly a beast out of the dim past, the ancient world of the dinosaurs and the giant tree ferns. What, I wondered, do the small reptilian brains make of these two-legged newcomers to their domain? But the alligator does not think; it

Young 'gators are little different in appearance from adults, except for size. Notice the slit-like pupil of the eye.

merely waits. It is not much different in appearance from the dead logs that also float upon the brown waters.

The alligators make their homes in the bayous or channels, but sometimes they prefer the large bodies of water. They excavate dens or 'gator holes in the banks below the water level, often of considerable size, perhaps twenty feet in length. Above the entrance to these caves, the 'gators sun themselves on smooth bars where the vegetation is worn away by their activities. In winter they retire to the 'gator holes to hibernate until the spring sun warms the marshland and stimulates them to emerge and find partners.

Mating of the alligators occurs in late winter or early spring, at which time there is considerable fighting, accompanied by mating calls which have been described as bellows but which are, in truth, moans or roars which drift across the marshland night for a mile or more. That the battles are vicious is evident from the fact that specimens with missing or mutilated legs and scars are common.

How big do alligators grow? This is a controversial matter. At first the young 'gators follow the cow, eating worms and insect life. Eventually they graduate to a diet of crayfish and, perhaps, frogs. It is a sad fact that large bullfrogs often capture and eat the baby 'gators, as do male alligators. The first year the young grow about five inches and by the end of the second year they reach about eighteen inches in length. At the age of seven years they average six feet and by the fourteenth year are perhaps twelve feet long and weigh about 650 pounds.

Large alligators are very powerful brutes and when fighting among themselves they clamp down upon each other's legs and attempt to twist them off by rolling over, an act that is often successful. When snapping at a rival the great jaws come together with a resounding bang that can be heard for some distance. With regard to the power of an alligator's jaws, I can do no better than quote the writings of E. A. McIlhenny, who knew the alligators of southern Louisiana better than any other man. He states:

> The crushing power of an alligator's jaws is enormous, and the muscular development operating the under jaw is tremendously heavy and strong. Whenever a three-foot alligator closes its jaws on an object it is impossible for a man with ordinary strength to open these jaws. When a large alligator closes its jaws on a victim, it is absolutely impossible, no matter what the strength of the thing grasped, for it to get away. This is the closing power of an alligator's jaws.

It is an unfortunate fact that alligators are no longer as common in the marshland as they once were; men and their guns destroy them for mere sport or sometimes for their skins. Certainly it will be a sad day for those of us who love and appreciate the wild inhabitants of the swamplands when the eerie bellow of the bull alligator no longer echoes across the marsh on warm nights in spring. The area will have lost something of its wild and primitive fascination.

Chapter 10

THE PALMETTO JUNGLE

THE PASCAGOULA FOLLOWS a tortuous channel in its unhurried approach to the Gulf; sometimes its banks are bordered by earthen ramparts rising high above the brown waters; at other times there are long stretches of fringing canebrakes and deep palmetto jungles. I had long been intrigued by a place several miles below The Island, on the opposite side of the river, where unusually large palmettos formed a dense wall of green reaching down to the water's edge and imparting a tropical atmosphere. High above the palmettos towered great trees standing in effortless repose, bound together with leafy vines. For some reason or other, which I was unable to explain, I was especially attracted to this place since it seemed to exude mystery; perhaps it was merely the lure of a remote and unknown place.

On one particular trip to The Island, I had as my personal helper a local character whose anonymity I shall guard by the appellation of L. C. Now L. C. considered himself to be a specialist in the care and feeding of outboard motors and alleged that there was very little about the mysterious workings of these motors he did not know. I, too, know all about such motors; I know, for example, that one is started by pulling vigorously on the starting rope while rapidly moving the throttle lever back and forth. If this fails to

The palmetto jungle beyond The Island consists of a dense growth of semi-tropical vegetation, dominated by fan palmettos. Spanish moss hangs from the trees.

194

stimulate the motor into throbbing life, the use of strong language, I have found, often has a most salutary effect.

At any rate, L. C. and I boarded one of the small boats and its outboard motor purred like a kitten at the first pull of the starter rope. We roared away from the houseboat and turned down the wide river, leaving an expanding wake behind us which rippled away to the banks, where its energy was dissipated in the fringing reeds which swayed violently for a time and then became quiet. Within a few minutes we arrived at our destination—the palmetto jungle. Our return, we were to find, was not destined to be so easy or so swift; but that part of the story comes later.

Having no idea what might be found in the dense growth of palmettos, I had loaded several cameras and miscellaneous collecting gear in the boat. When on an expedition of this sort it never pays to be without basic equipment. Too often I have seen interesting or unusual plants or animals while without the means of collecting or photographing them, a most disgusting state of affairs to a biologist.

Arriving at the growth of palmettos, we ran the bow of the boat up among a tangle of tree roots along the bank and I climbed out and tied the craft securely. L. C. had brought along a cane pole and a can of worms, so he at once set about trying his luck.

Everything seemed to be under control at the boat so I lifted my camera cases and other equipment ashore and pushed inland through the dense, jungle-like growth. Progress was very slow since the palmetto fronds reached far above my head like great, spreading fans and the ground was soft and saturated with water. Interspersed among the palmettos grew oak and titi trees, all festooned with the usual heavy growth of Spanish moss. Here and there I encountered shallow pools of clear water around which I was forced to detour. Now and again the way was often blocked by spiny vines and other vegetation through which I hacked my way with a machete. At the same time, I kept a sharp lookout for snakes. These creatures are not usually a problem but this looked like moccasin and rattlesnake territory and I was taking no chances.

Everywhere around me as I pushed through the dense, semi-

Left: *The fronds of the palmettos are fan-like and stiff, often a yard across. They arise near the ground.* Right: *In autumn, black berries mature on spreading stalks of the fan palmettos. Each one contains a hard seed which will germinate in the moist soil.*

tropical vegetation stood the palmettos, their leaf stems arising from crowns only a foot above the moist earth. For those who are not familiar with palmettos, I should, perhaps, furnish a little information about them. The fan palmettos found in this area are known to botanists as *Sabal minor* and are the only representatives of the palm family found growing wild along this portion of the Gulf Coast. Unlike the more truly tropical palms, fan palmettos have their fronds arising near the ground, not from the tops of the tall trunks. The crowns from which fan palmetto fronds arise are attached to subterranean rootstocks and, in summer, a stem pushes up out of the crown, bearing at its top a cluster of inconspicuous blooms which, in time, give rise to black, berry-like fruit containing hard, spherical seeds. The leaf stems of these palmettos are very hard and stiff and the great fan-like leaves or fronds are held nearly erect. The truth is, of course, that a fan palmetto is merely a palm tree with a very short trunk, probably an adaptation to life in a climate that is less than tropical. If one were to cut off the crown of a Florida cabbage palmetto with its attached fronds and set it in the ground, it would resemble very closely a local fan palmetto. Actually, the trunks of some tropical palms, such as the nipa palm, grow along beneath the soil, sending up graceful fronds from their tips. These are the palm fronds used in the South Pacific for thatching native huts.

As I forced my way between the crowded palmetto clumps, the fronds made loud rattling sounds; it was impossible to progress silently. This was unfortunate since, in order to see wild creatures, it is necessary to move slowly and without sound. Of course, whether we admit it or not, almost all wild creatures have ears so sensitive that a man tiptoeing through a forest sounds like a herd of elephants on a wild stampede. I once read about a man who set up a sensitive listening device in a forest where hunters were silently (they thought) stalking game. Even though the hunters were moving slowly and carefully, the sensitive electronic instrument amplified the sounds they made so that every footfall and every disturbed leaf was clearly heard. The electronic listening device had merely increased the sensitivity of the experimenter's ears, making them equal to those of wild creatures. What was especially interesting in this test was that while the experimenter was hidden in the forest with his instrument a small pack of wolves passed a short distance away—at about the same distance that the human hunters had passed—but made no sounds that could be detected on the sensitive listening device, thus proving that wild creatures can move silently.

Even though I often walk through forests in what I hope is almost complete silence, I know that I am the only creature that is being deceived. Everywhere, sensitive ears listen to my steps and hidden eyes follow my progress. We humans have gradually lost the sensory abilities with which our ears and eyes were once endowed. It has been a long while since our very lives depended upon our hearing and seeing acuity.

As I cautiously pushed on into the dark, gloomy palmetto growth I became increasingly conscious of a sense of complete isolation.

The fan-like fronds towering above me and the Spanish moss draped from every tree had the combined effect of absorbing all sounds emanating from beyond the immediate vicinity. Though I made every effort to move cautiously and make little sound, my progress was heralded by rasping sounds, so I had but little hope of seeing much wildlife. There were, of course, creeping things of small size; crawling over the damp ground I saw a millipede as long as a pencil, its numerous legs moving in unison as it moved along like a miniature train. Snails, too, glided slowly over leaves and damp earth, their soft bodies extended and their stalked eyes bending now and again to examine the surfaces over which they passed.

Resting upon the ground across a small opening was a fallen tree, now in an advanced stage of decay. Since dead logs always fascinate me, I chopped into the soft, rotting wood. At first I saw nothing of interest, but when a piece of bark on the opposite side was pried off, a scorpion was exposed, its sting-bearing tail raised over its back in a threatening pose. Desiring the specimen for photography, I

Hidden beneath the bark of a fallen log was a scorpion, its tail armed with a poisonous sting. But the sting of this scorpion is little more serious than that of a hornet.

A colorful but poisonous coral snake crawls slowly across the ground. Its body is encircled by alternating bands of scarlet, yellow, and black, and its venom is neurotoxic.

clapped a jar over it and secured the lid. The right end of the log was much softer than the rest so I pushed my machete into the yielding wood and pried off a large section. Deeper down, where the wood was damp with decay, I noticed some bright red object and, having no idea what it might be, I probed it with the tip of the machete exposing, much to my surprise, an eighteen-inch coral snake. It was beautiful; its slender body was encircled with alternating bands of scarlet, yellow, and black, and its snout was black. This latter coloring definitely identified it as a coral snake rather than a scarlet snake, which is similarly marked.

Obtaining a short stick, I lifted the pretty snake from the decaying wood and dropped it on the ground. At first, it made no effort to strike but when touched with the stick it eventually seized it and hung on so that I was able to lift it from the ground.

The coral snake, *Micrurus*, is relatively common in this area and its bite is highly poisonous. It does not strike after the manner of the rattlers and moccasins but bites and hangs on so as to allow its nerve-destroying venom to seep into the wound made by its short fangs.

These snakes may cause the deaths of children since they are pretty and attractive. A child may often play with a coral snake for some time before it eventually bites. I once talked to a forest ranger who had discovered his small daughter playing with one of these snakes. It had not bitten her. Picking up a stick, he prodded the creature and eventually induced it to bite it. The ranger then killed the snake and walked off, still carrying the stick. Unconsciously, he handled the stick and apparently got the venom on his hands; in some fashion it came in contact with his mouth. The result was that his mouth was paralyzed and numb for several hours due to the neurotoxic nature of the coral snake's venom.

Having no container in which to carry the snake, I left it by the fallen tree and walked on. At one point I paused near a pool of water to mop my brow and examine my surroundings. I could no longer hear the sounds of the river but, as well as I could determine, I had been walking in a more or less straight line away from it. From a cypress towering high overhead there came the loud, discordant call of a pileated woodpecker and I glanced upward where its brilliant red topknot bobbed along a limb. Then, a sound on the ground beyond a cypress "knee" attracted my attention and, when I stepped over to investigate, I saw to my surprise a diamondback rattlesnake coiled upon the damp earth. It was at least five feet in length, but this, at the moment, was difficult to estimate since it was tightly coiled. Along the back of its heavy, muscular body was a series of diamond-shaped markings; but it was the head especially that attracted my attention. It was broad with white lines above the eyes, eyes that focused on me through narrow, vertical pupils. From among the coils, on the opposite side, its tail, tipped with a long series of rattles, was extended. At first, these rattles were quiet but, when I moved for a closer look, they went into violent action with a buzzing sound that can strike fear into the heart of the most experienced biologist. It was, I knew, not an empty threat.

There in the palmetto jungle we regarded each other, the snake and I. The snake, I think, had no fear and was ready and well able to defend itself. It lay quietly coiled there in the dim light of the deep forest and I was acutely conscious of its immense potential for ferocity. For my part, I treated my opponent with extreme respect since a large diamondback is, without doubt, the most dangerous reptile on the continent of North America. Because of its great size, its poison glands contain considerable venom and its fangs are longer in proportion than those of any other poisonous snake in this country. Its bite is often fatal, frequently within an hour's time. It is a very dangerous snake, especially if the person is bitten far from medical help. I recalled a case where a man, crawling through dense vegetation, had been struck in the face by a large diamondback and died within minutes.

Altogether, the snake was an evil-appearing creature, one that I had no desire to molest. From a distance of five feet I looked closely

Left: *Upon the jungle floor rests a coiled diamondback rattlesnake, probably the most deadly of all American snakes. Possible death awaits the unwary traveler.* Right: *Found also in the palmetto jungle are timber rattlers, almost as deadly as the diamondbacks.*

The fangs of the rattlesnake are hollow, hypodermic teeth that, when at rest, are folded back against the roof of the mouth. Periodically, new fangs (upper right) slip into place, replacing the old fangs which are shed.

at its vicious head; beyond the nostrils, I could easily see the deep pits believed to be sensory in function, probably as temperature detectors. By means of these organs a rattlesnake can probably detect the nearby presence of a warm-blooded animal such as a rabbit. These pits are also used by biologists in their classification; both rattlesnakes and moccasins possess them and so are called pit vipers. The coral snake, on the other hand, belongs to a different family.

For perhaps three minutes I watched the snake but it made no move to leave; it was in its native domain and I was the intruder. Once or twice I placed my hand on the pistol at my belt but each time changed my mind. Evil and dangerous as it was, it was one of the characteristic inhabitants of the swamp and at last I elected to leave it there. Tossing a clod of earth at the snake caused it to un-

Above: *This copperhead moccasin rests quietly on the jungle floor, its attractive coloration blending with the light and shadow. Its bite, too, is dangerous.* Left: *This close-up view shows the details of a copperhead's head. Note the oval shape of its pupil and the sensory pit between the eye and the nostril.*

coil slowly and crawl away beneath the palmettos, retreating with dignity and poise.

With greatly increased caution, I pushed on deeper into the jungle and began to notice various places where the earth had been dug up. I suspected this to be the result of the wild hogs that inhabit these lowlands. These hogs are fairly common and are not really

wild hogs at all but domestic hogs that have lived for many generations in the forests, subsisting on acorns and roots. Now and then
I paused to listen and, from just beyond a particularly dense patch
of vegetation, I thought I could hear some animal scratching or
digging. Making as little noise as possible, I moved on among the
palmettos, pausing occasionally to listen. I could still hear the
sounds. At last I came to an area of tall grass in an open glade in
the forest and stopped again. The sounds were closer now and,
seemingly, originated in the grass, but I could see no movement.

Making sure that the pistol at my belt was loaded, I walked
slowly ahead. If it was indeed a wild hog, I had no desire to face an
angry boar unarmed, since I had heard tales of people actually
being attacked in these swamps. Near the edge of the grassy area
lay a fallen tree and, climbing upon this in order to get a better
view, I looked down into the grass, where I saw what was apparently the slate-gray back of a hog busily rooting in the earth and at
the same time making small snuffling sounds. For a minute or so I
watched but saw only this one individual, which was certainly
small for a hog. It could, of course, be a young pig, but if so, what
was it doing alone? I was puzzled, but continued my vigil on top of
the log. After a few minutes the animal began moving through the
grass in my direction and, eventually, much to my surprise, a slender
snout poked out from among the grass stems, followed by a head
surmounted by pig-like ears. But it was not a pig at all! Into the
open slowly ambled a full-grown armadillo, one of the most remarkable creatures found in the United States. Until a few years
ago, the range of these strange animals extended only as far eastward
as Louisiana. Armadillos are also found in Florida, probably having
escaped from captivity. Indeed, once they were found only in
Texas and southward into Mexico. In recent years, however, they
have spread eastward and crossed the Mississippi River. Just how
they crossed this great stream is a mystery; perhaps they took advantage of the bridges when these were built to replace the old
ferries.

Here in its newly adopted territory, the armadillo seems an alien creature, not really a proper part of the fauna. Usually the first time one is seen, the reaction is that there just couldn't be any such animal. I had seen mounted specimens, of course, but it is one thing to see a stuffed armadillo and quite another to observe the living creature going about its business in the wild. Yet, here was one on the ground below me shuffling about as if undecided what to do next. My reaction was more or less automatic; I made a flying tackle and grabbed the armadillo! However, I must admit that the surprise was mutual. The armadillo suddenly went into violent action, attempting to escape, but my own surprise was of another sort. I knew the armadillo to be a warm-blooded mammal rather closely related to the anteaters, that it bears living young and lives upon ants and other insects. I knew all these facts, yet, when my hands actually came in contact with its turtle-like back I was astonished to discover that it was warm! I suppose that since the armadillo's back was hard and smooth like that of a turtle I had expected it would feel cold to the touch. However illogical my reaction, I was indeed surprised.

The armadillo has only recently spread its domain into the region of The Island. It is closely related to the tropical anteaters and, like them, feeds on insects. Its body is covered with hinged plates.

Successfully capturing the armadillo, I next wondered what to do with it. Optimistically, I considered that perhaps I could tame it and keep it as an unusual pet. Against such optimism, I recalled numerous other pets including foxes, 'coons, and bullfrogs whose domestication had turned out far less than successful. Regardless of past experience, I decided to carry the armadillo along, leaving the decision as to its ultimate fate to the future. This, of course, posed some problems since I was already loaded down with cameras and other gear. However, I carried it along by its convenient handle, the tail.

Later, back at my home, I did everything possible to make the armadillo happy; I dug for grubs and gathered ants, assuming such items to be its normal food, but the cantankerous creature would eat none of the choice insects I offered, apparently preferring to forage on its own. I use the term "its" advisedly since I was never able to learn whether it was male or female; however, I presumed this to be an unimportant matter except, perhaps, to another armadillo. Armadillos have rather peculiar reproductive habits that are in keeping with their other unusual characteristics; the females always bear four young, all of the same sex. Since these arise from one fertilized egg cell, they are always identical quadruplets.

While in captivity, my armadillo showed little inclination toward domestication and when liberated in my backyard it made every effort to escape. In one way, at least, the creature was quite shrewd. Several times I released it from its cage, allowing it to walk about while being held by its tail. For several minutes it would amble along, apparently unconscious of the grip I had on its posterior extremity. Then, when least expected, it would suddenly dart forward, jerking its tail from my grasp.

On occasion, I turned it loose in my wife's flower beds, where it immediately tunneled into the soft earth so that only its tail remained visible. This, being harmful to the flowers, did little to endear it to my wife so, in the end, I was forced to return the armadillo to its native haunts where I assume it still lives.

Making my way back through the palmetto jungle with the

struggling armadillo held by the tail, I arrived at the place where L. C. was *supposed* to be. It was certainly the place where we had tied up the boat, as I verified by examining the surroundings. Still, the boat was nowhere in sight. What to do? Here I was, isolated in a patch of jungle on the opposite side of the river with no means whatever of getting back to the houseboat. Infrequently, fishermen in motorboats passed up and down the river; perhaps I could hail one. My indignation gradually increased to the boiling point and, at last, I began to yell loudly for L. C. I could not understand why he had left me marooned.

After ten minutes or so, I was overjoyed to hear a paddle dipping in the water around a bend of the river and soon L. C. nonchalantly appeared. When he was within speaking distance I inquired as to

Farther inland, the jungle is even more dense, and progress through it is very difficult. In many respects, it resembles a hammock of the Everglades.

The bayou channels are often bordered with growths of arrowhead or Sagittaria, characterized by arrow-shaped leaves and white blooms.

where he had been and was informed that he had "naturally" assumed that I would be busy in the palmetto jungle for the remainder of the day; he had gone fishing at a favorite spot farther down the river. I had some thoughts of my own on the subject but, fortunately, was able to keep them to myself.

Having placed the armadillo in a convenient sack and stowed it in the boat along with my gear, we cranked up the motor and went on down the river. We passed beside margins of jungle millet and other tall marsh grasses until we arrived at the entrance to Swift Bayou, a channel perhaps twenty feet wide leading away into the savannah toward the east. There was no particular reason for choosing this bayou; it merely looked like a good place to explore.

The channel meandered through the tall grass and I noticed smaller channels branching away at intervals. The motor was running perfectly and all seemed well. One side channel appeared wider than most so I signaled L. C. to cut the motor and enter it. We now resorted to paddles, since I wished to explore the narrow opening with as little noise as possible. Just beyond the entrance, this branch widened out into a sizable channel with sloping mud flats along its margins. Here numerous footprints of raccoons were in evidence. Once I saw a rail walking along among the clustered stems of the marsh grasses, and at another place a purple gallinule stood quietly beneath a small cypress, its rich purple color in striking contrast to the pastel shades of the marsh. At our closer approach, the attractive bird evidenced alarm by twitching motions of its short tail. This is probably the most beautiful bird found in these savannahs; in addition to the vivid coloration of its body feathers, the base of its bill is blood-red, the remainder being bright yellow. Nature was, indeed, lavish with her palate when she painted this bird!

At our approach the gallinule lifted itself from the mud on beating wings and flew down the bayou ahead of us with a weak fluttering flight, its chrome-yellow legs dangling just above the water. At the same time it uttered its characteristic *kek*, *kek*, *kek* call, then disappeared from view around a bend like some bright spirit, leaving the feeling that perhaps it had never existed.

We pushed the bow of the boat up on a mud flat and I stepped out, cautioning L. C. in no uncertain terms to remain there while I explored the territory away from the channel. The tide was out and the bases of the tall marsh vegetation rested in exposed muck that, while wet, would still support my weight. By the time I had advanced only a few yards the green, grassy world closed in around me on all sides and the only audible sounds were those of marsh birds and soft rustlings of the twelve-foot grasses as they swayed in the breeze.

From some vague point farther away through the grass I could hear splashing sounds and, assuming that there was evidently open water nearby, I pushed on, cautiously stepping, wherever possible, on grassy clumps to keep from sinking into the mud. After going but a few yards I saw water shining through the grass and could still hear the splashing sounds. There was undoubtedly something disturbing the water but, from my present location, I could see nothing, so quietly moved on again. Soon I reached a point where I had an unobstructed view of a watery expanse, a pool perhaps thirty feet across. I could see no sign of life, yet the splashing sounds continued, coming now from the left side of the pool which was obscured from view by marsh grass.

I crouched down and waited. A pair of red-winged blackbirds sailed down and perched for a time on the swaying tips of giant foxtail grasses or jungle millet, then flew away. Still I waited and was shortly rewarded by one of the most charming sights imaginable. Against the dull-colored background of mud there swam into view a pair of wood ducks, the male gorgeously arrayed in every color of the rainbow. The heads of both ducks were crowned with crests but that of the male glistened with deep green and purple marked by narrow white lines. His back was metallic-green. His mate, by contrast, was of more somber hues; yet, together, there in the quiet pool they made a most elegant pair as they swam slowly along, totally unconscious of my presence.

Linnaeus, who gave the wood duck its generic name, *sponsa*, recognized its beauty, since the Latin name, freely translated, means "dressed in bridal vesture." It should be understood, of course, that the colorful "bride" is actually the male.

Wood ducks range over much of North America and, wherever found, their regal beauty is appreciated by bird-lovers. Unusual among ducks are their nesting habits; they choose hollows in trees, most often those growing in or near water. For many years, a controversy raged among ornithologists as to how the flightless young got down to the water from nest holes often fifty feet above the ground. One school of thought believed that the downy young simply jumped out of the nest and floated down like huge snowflakes; another school stated just as positively that the mother carried them down, one at a time, in her bill. Fortunately the matter has now been settled by direct observation; the young simply scramble down the tree trunks, using their sharp claws to hang onto the bark. Once on the water, they paddle along with their mother, as is the habit of most other ducklings.

The pair of wood ducks swam along over the surface of the pool while, from my place of concealment, I watched in fascinated admiration. Eventually I raised up for a better view, but the birds saw me at once and took to the air with a loud splashing that sent bright droplets of water flying in the sun.

Returning to the boat, we paddled on along the channel, which was now bordered with growths of duck potato in full bloom with spikes of white flowers. Gradually the way narrowed to a point where progress was difficult so L. C. and I decided that we should turn about and crank up the motor. No luck! We waited a few minutes, then tried again with the same dismal outcome.

But one course now seemed open, to paddle the boat back out into the bayou and then a mile upstream on the river to the houseboat. This we did with what Sir Winston Churchill would, perhaps, have described as the shedding of "blood, toil, tears, and sweat."

An hour later back at the houseboat, safely tied to a cypress "knee," L. C. tried cranking the motor again. Much to my disgust it immediately roared into throbbing life, leaving me with a foul opinion of outboard motors in general and of this one in particular.

Chapter 11

AFTER THE SUNSET

ONCE EACH DAY, darkness floods across The Island, transforming the sunlit world into one of obscurity. Slowly, as the light drains away toward the west, the day-loving creatures retire to hidden retreats, leaving island and marshland to those that prefer the night. The darkness also has its effect on the plants. If I were able to watch them in slow motion, I would find that the leaves of many kinds rise during the day and fall during the night. These are called "sleep movements" and are caused by variations in the water content of the leaves which, in turn, is influenced by alterations in light intensity.

In the more shady portions of The Island grow patches of wood sorrel *(Oxalis)*. Its leaves resemble those of clover; each one is made up of three leaflets. At dusk these leaflets fold up and remain so until the forest is flooded by morning light. There is also a lone mimosa tree, grown no doubt from a seed carried to The Island by some bird. Each evening its numerous leaflets fold themselves together in sleep. In less obvious ways, almost all the trees and plants take time out from their daily work of manufacturing foods. If I could study the living leaves of almost any plant under a microscope at night I would find that most of its stomates or breathing pores had closed. While sunlight pours down on the leaves, they are busy making starch and the excess water is passing out of the open stomates as vapor but, with the coming of darkness, these manufacturing centers cease operation and most of the stomates close.

For many millions of years, plants and animals have lived under conditions of approximately half darkness and half light with the result that many of them have evolved deep-seated adaptations. Many animals, for example, follow daily cycles of activity that are not mere responses to the presence or absence of light but which have slowly become a part of their physiology. If a person, for example, is isolated in a cave with no contact with the outside world, his daily living habits will tend to follow approximately the usual twenty-four-hour cycle. This is called the *circadian* rhythm, a term meaning "about a day." Many of The Island's living things follow this circadian rhythm and would continue to do so even if kept in complete darkness or continuous light.

These alternating periods of light and dark have been regularly following each other for so long that many plants and animals have been modified to enable them to live in one or the other. Here on The Island I do not have far to look for an excellent example. Owls are birds of the night, well fitted to activity after sunset; only rarely are they on the wing during the day. Sometimes, on my excursions across The Island, I see them perched quietly in trees and they usually fly away at my approach. While their vision is adequate for daytime flight, they are at their best during the dusk and it is then that they hunt their game. Their eyes are especially fitted for seeing in dim light, both being oriented forward like our own, unlike those of most other birds which are placed on either side of the head. Since both of an owl's eyes cover the same visual field, their sensitivity is increased and they can see better in dim light. In addition, its eyes are very large. If its eyes are observed during the day they appear to be dull and glazed, but this is because, in bright light, a protective light shield is drawn across them. Known as the *nictitating* membrane, or "third eyelid," this semitransparent shield is pulled back during the night, greatly increasing the owl's ability to see. It is, indeed, a remarkable adaptation and enables these birds to hunt for mice which are nocturnal in habit.

Thus, some creatures such as owls have abandoned the day and become creatures of the night. On the other hand, most animals are

The eyes of owls are especially adapted to vision in dim light. During the day, thin membranes close across their sensitive eyes, protecting them from bright light. Shown here is an owl with the protective membranes partly closed.

active only during the hours of daylight and enter the unconscious condition we call sleep when darkness comes. Most birds such as mockingbirds and cardinals belong in this category. In some ways sleep is similar to hibernation; both conditions enable animals to survive periods unfavorable to normal activity.

Physiologists and psychologists have devoted considerable effort to the study of sleep, yet it still remains one of the mysteries of the brain. It seems that by now such a common thing as sleep would long since have been understood, but the truth is that so far we have only theories. Formerly, biologists believed that sleep was brought about by an accumulation of fatigue products such as lactic acid. More recently, another theory has been propounded. According to this postulation, there is a substance called *hypnotoxin* produced by the brain and which acts like a narcotic. There is good experimental evidence to prove that this is so. On the other hand, many biologists believe that wakefulness is caused by a high degree of activity

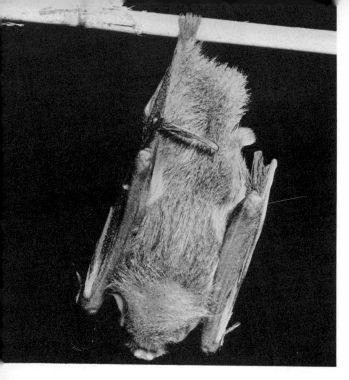

During daylight hours, bats, with their wings folded, hang from twigs and tall grass stems. At dusk they leave their perches and fly among the trees and over the river, capturing insects.

in the cerebrum—the conscious portion of the brain—while sleep results when this activity decreases. At any rate, during sleep most body functions decrease, blood pressure is reduced, respiration slows down, the heart beats less rapidly, while digestive processes continue at their normal rates.

Sleep, the strange condition of unconsciousness into which most animals lapse each night, is one in which active life decreases, awaiting the coming of another day, that period when the animal's location on the earth again faces the sun. Sleep has resulted from cosmic forces operating over millions of years and it enables day-living animals to survive the nights when they cannot feed or move about with freedom.

Most of us fear the darkness, especially in deep forests or other unknown places such as The Island. It is a fear that is as old as the human race and it is easy to imagine primitive man cringing in his cave after the long, dark night had set in. Beyond the confines of his refuge prowled dark and furtive enemies that he could not see but only imagine, and the fact of their invisibility made them a

Navigating among the branches of trees, the bats use echo-location techniques. High-pitched sounds emitted from their throats are reflected back to sensitive ears from limbs or flying insects, thus aiding in aerial navigation and in capturing food.

thousand times more terrifying. Thus, it is not at all surprising that early men became sun worshipers; the sun became the symbol of life and the night became the abode of demons. Civilized as we consider ourselves to be, we cannot throw off this primitive fear of darkness which is merely that period of the day when our portion of the earth is turned away from the sun.

Probably the most satisfying part of the day on The Island, to me at least, comes at twilight after the sun sinks beyond the western savannahs and the sky turns crimson just ahead of the flowing tide of darkness. The heat of the day has gone and cool breezes blow inland from the Gulf; the streamers of moss suspended from the trees sway in unison and the evening songs of birds are heard. As the dusk settles down, the first call of the barred owl echoes across the wide river and the sound has a quality both elemental and primitive, reminding the human visitor that he has invaded a place that is wild and remote. Again and again comes the eerie call, each time seemingly ending in demoniac laughter, and as I listen, chills chase each other up my spine, The call of the owl is the harbinger of darkness, the reminder that the daylight has gone. Slowly the darkness gathers in the deep island forest like a black fog, then spreads out to encompass the river. Some evenings in summer the river is tinted crimson by the sky, reflecting its mood; at other times night comes without fanfare or color, especially when storm clouds are banked darkly against the western sky and the horizon is obscured by rain.

On a number of occasions I have found a comfortable seat on The Island and watched with interest the arrival of dusk, reveling in the feeling of complete isolation. With the approach of night the damp smells of the forest rise from the ground, redolent of rotting wood, decaying leaves, and the fragrance of moist earth. This is my favorite part of the twenty-four-hour period on The Island, yet during this quiet time I find myself unconsciously watching for unknown shapes in the deeper shadows, and from hidden recesses of my mind creep ancient fears of the coming night.

The cicada chorus has long since been stilled and soon the first

Katydids, perched in trees, saw out their tunes in the twilight. During the day, their vivid green coloration affords protection from most enemies.

katydids tune up their fiddles and burst out in full song. Now one individual begins, then another, until the forest rings with the sounds. Then they all fade away as if some unseen conductor were directing their performance. From high above the forest, now and again I hear the sounds of nighthawks in their steep dives through the air, and over the dusky river I see swallows darting like arrows in pursuit of insects. Sometimes a swallow actually touches the water, creating a small ripple ring that expands and fades away over the dark water. Tonight, as I watch, the river is tinged with red like the sky and I cannot tell where one leaves off and the other begins; river and sky seem united into a crimson pool without end or beginning. I have often noticed this same illusion when returning to The Island at dusk in a motorboat; water and sky are joined together and the boat seems not to be floating on the water but cruising through a rosy medium that is neither water nor air; space and time lose their meanings.

Animals are classified as being diurnal, nocturnal, or crepuscular in habit. Diurnal, from the Latin word *diurnalis*, means "of the day;" while crepuscular is derived from *crepusculum*, also a Latin word, pertaining to twilight. Crepuscular animals are those that are active at dusk. As dusk is gradually replaced by night, a different group of animals comes on duty. These are nocturnal in habits and this term too is derived from Latin, *nocturnalis* meaning "of the night." Thus, the day is divided into three parts, the daylight hours, the dusk, and the night, during each of which different animals become active. I once traveled for a hundred miles through a heavily forested but thinly settled area. At dusk, many deer were seen along the highway and swamp rabbits often crossed the road. As the light faded, 'possums and raccoons were in evidence and a prowling bobcat was seen. Moths, attracted by the car's headlights, banged against the windshield. Animal life of many kinds was on the move, hunting for food or, perhaps, for mates. I had expected that as it became later at night, more and more wild creatures would be seen, but in this I was disappointed. By midnight the forest through which I traveled was almost entirely devoid of life except for an occasional moth. Evidently the wild creatures of the forest had all, by that time, satisfied their appetites and gone to bed and I had the highway to myself.

With regard to the activity of night-flying insects, I once carried out an interesting piece of research. Since I am lazy by nature and unwilling to stay up all night, I constructed a light trap designed in such a way that insects attracted by the light and captured in jars during each two-hour period of the night would be kept separate. This trap was operated during many nights and the results were most interesting. Leaf hoppers were most abundant between the hours from 7 to 11 P.M., after which they decreased until 3 A.M., when they again become active. Wasps of several kinds were captured throughout the night but increased in abundance as the night progressed. Winged male and female ants appeared during the early morning hours beginning at 3 A.M. Beetles are always attracted to light traps and, in this experiment, their activity continued until after midnight when they gradually disappeared.

This little experiment proved that, among nocturnal insects, there are definite periods of greatest activity. On one night, 384 beetles were captured between 7 and 9 P.M., none between 9 and 11 P.M., while 192 were captured between 11 P.M. and 1 A.M. Why this occurred I can only guess; perhaps an unfavorable weather condition influenced the activity of the beetles near midnight.

In general, my results from the light-trap experiment were similar to earlier research carried out in England by Dr. C. B. Williams, the well-known authority on insect migration. Dr. Williams found that, in general, insect activity decreases during the night. He did discover one most interesting fact; in the case of some moths, the females were on the wing earlier in the night than the males.

There are few nocturnal mammals on The Island; occasionally raccoons visit it and I have seen the footprints of 'possums. Sometimes on quiet, nighttime forays I have glimpsed the illusive forms of white-footed mice skipping along on the ground beside fallen

Toads hop across the ground at night searching for insect food. They add their rasping voices to the multitudinous sounds of the night.

After dark, white-footed mice emerge from hiding places in hollow logs and search for seeds on the forest floor. Often, they are captured by owls that drop down out of the trees.

logs. These mice are much more attractive than their cousins that invade our households. Clean in habits and dressed in soft fur that is snow-white beneath and brown above, they feed upon seeds and other woodland fare. Like other nocturnal animals, their eyes are larger than normal and no doubt they can see well in dim light. Never abroad during the daylight hours, they forage in the dusk and the darkness when all is quiet. Even in complete darkness they can still find their way about by means of long sensitive whiskers, or vibrissae, and sensitive ears. Sometimes, while sitting in the moonlight, I have perceived them darting across open, sandy glades, but always there was a question as to whether or not they were inventions of my imagination; they seemed as formless as the moonbeams filtering down through the foliage of the trees.

White-footed mice *(Peromyscus)* build their nests in hollow logs, forming them of fine grasses and down. Several times I have exposed their nests, while chopping into rotten logs, and have seen their young. Always, the mother was present but quickly made her escape by darting into a nearby hole. From the speed of her disappearance and the certainty with which she darted for the hole, I had no doubt but that she knew every suitable refuge in the immediate vicinity. The life of a mouse must certainly depend on a knowledge of many alternate escape routes since it has numerous enemies. Out of the night on silent wings drop hunting owls with eyes even more sensitive than theirs; the numerous regurgitated owl pellets I have seen in the forest bear mute evidence of the toll taken of the mouse population; every pellet contained the gray fur and white bones of woodland mice. An owl's capture of a mouse is a silent affair; the feathers of the bird are soft and fluffy, making no sound as it sails down from the tree; one moment the mouse is darting across the dry leaves, then mysteriously it has disappeared and the owl moves off as silently as before.

The most fascinating nights on The Island occur in summer when the full moon hangs like a great yellow ball above the forest. I have roamed the island woods at such times, reveling in its mystery and its strange allure. Beneath the soft light of the moon, the most commonplace things such as trees, logs and stumps take on weird forms and the imagination transforms them into unknown beasts. Here beside the trail a rotting stump is surmounted by a clump of ferns. I have seen this stump many times and have even examined its surface for slime molds, yet tonight it is a dark, foreboding form that could be anything from a bear to a wild hog. If I watch it closely, it even appears to move, so I turn my flashlight on just to make sure that what I am seeing is really the stump. Assured that it is the familiar object, I turn off my light and am soon aware that the moon has been obscured by a dark cloud and that the forest is now in almost total darkness. I glance at the stump once more and am astonished; its surface now glows with a strange greenish light and this, of course, is something that must be investigated further. With my machete, I chop off a fragment of the soft wood and hold it in my hand. The fragment continues to glow and I am surprised also to find that some of the phosphorescent substance has rubbed off on my fingers.

What I am seeing, I know, is fox fire, but this does little to dispel the creepy feeling brought about by this strange luminous stump deep in the dark island forest. Certainly encountering this fox fire in ancient times must have inspired fear in ignorant people. Only a few times during my life have I had opportunity of observing fox fire firsthand. I have seen it along the margins of bayous and streams as I traveled by boat, and someone once brought me a piece of rotten wood containing fox fire. In each case the greenish light emanating from the decaying wood glowed eerily.

I chop off a piece of the stump and later observe it in my studio, where it continues to emit light for several days until quite dry. When water is added, it again glows in the darkness and I am able to keep the light-producing fungus alive for several weeks. There are many different fungi or rotten-wood molds that glow in the dark, as well as certain bacteria. Probably the most common light-producing bacteria are found on dead fish and decaying meats. Growths of phosphorescent bacteria have also been seen on cheese. Perhaps the earliest observer of these luminous bacteria was Fabricius ab Aquapendente at Padua, who saw their glow on mutton in 1592.

Since this particular night on The Island seems favorable for the growth of fox-fire fungus on rotting wood, I extend my excursion farther inland and am elated to find other instances. Apparently the recent rain and the warm night are conducive to the abundant growth of luminescent fungi.

It has usually been my experience that when conditions are favorable for some phenomenon, one had best take advantage of them; otherwise opportunities for interesting observations may be lost. The night is humid and, most of the time, the full moon remains hidden behind heavy clouds. Occasionally there are flashes of lightning on the distant horizon but it is so far away that I cannot hear the sound of thunder. From my right comes the gentle lapping of the river and the hissing sounds of the marsh grasses. From the river, also, I can sometimes hear mysterious plops and splashes but I have no idea what causes them; they are a part of the island night and I accept them, only half-conscious that they exist at all.

Growing near the edge of a small pool is a large clump of palmettos. Into this jungle-like growth I make my way, turning on my flashlight at times to find an opening. The palmettos reach high above my head and sometimes I am forced to clear away the elaborate webs of orb-weaving spiders built in geometric designs across the open spaces. Such quiet summer nights, I have found, are usually favorable for spider web construction.

Beyond the palmettos lies a large rotten log surrounded by broken limbs and I examine it for evidence of luminescent molds. There is no sign of any glow so I have about decided to retrace my steps when my eyes are attracted by a faint, greenish light emanating from the opposite side of the log. Looking over the top I am astonished to see a clump of mushrooms gleaming brightly in the darkness. For several moments I look at them, marveling that they produce sufficient light to outline their forms distinctly. Even the dead leaves beneath them are dimly illuminated. Turning on my flashlight, I find them to be orange-yellow in hue and about six inches tall. Some of them have just emerged from the ground and their caps are not yet expanded. I pull one mature specimen up and turn it over to discover that the gills on its undersurface are even more luminescent than the rest of the mushroom.

What I have discovered is a clump of jack-o'-lantern mushrooms (*Clitocybe illudens*) which are often found growing on or near old stumps or decaying logs. These strange mushrooms are poisonous if eaten, causing nausea and vomiting. They emit light most brilliantly when freshly emerged from the ground; it gradually fades as they dry up.

Light produced by plants and animals is "cold light"; that is, it is light produced without accompanying heat as in the case of an electric light bulb. Called *bioluminescence*, or "living light," it is pro-

Fireflies flit through the dusk, flashing their lights at intervals. Sometimes they alight on twigs and light their lanterns.

duced by a wide variety of living things and, in most instances, there appears to be no practical reason for it. Of what possible use to the mushrooms can light production be? Neither does there appear to be any reason why certain bacteria produce light. On the other hand, light production by fireflies does have a practical significance; the flashes of light emitted by both the males and females aid in bringing the sexes together for mating. The male fireflies flit about through the forest, now and again flashing their lanterns, while the females resting in the grass give answering flashes. Fireflies of different species use different codes so that females are only stimulated to give answering flashes to males of their own species. But, if we follow this line of reasoning, how do we explain the fact that glow-worms, which are immature fireflies, also emit light? Why, also, are firefly eggs luminescent? Such questions have been raised by many biologists but, as yet, there appear to be few answers.

To our ancestors, phosphorescent molds and bacteria were evidences of strange and unknown forces and naturally were regarded with superstitious fear. Even in my own case, this strange light, whether that of the common firefly or the eerie glow of luminescent molds, gives me the feeling that I am confronted by some supernatural force. I may tell myself that what I am seeing is merely an interesting chemical reaction, but this does little to dispel its mystery and I am still amazed. While we are still ignorant about many aspects of this "living light" we have learned a good deal about the chemistry of its production. It has been found that at least two substances are involved; a material called *luciferine* is oxidized in the presence of an enzyme called *luciferase*. This reaction produces light.

Recently, in my laboratory, I came across a tiny vial containing small, dried crustaceans from the sea. I have had this vial for several years and finally decided on an experiment. I placed a few of the tiny crustaceans in a dish, covered them with warm water and then turned out the lights. Even though these little animals were dead and had been in storage for so long, the addition of water caused each one to glow with light.

The crustaceans referred to were *Cypridina*, which are common in various parts of the world, especially in the sea near Japan where fishermen call them "sea fireflies." When touched, the living animals emit brilliant flashes of bluish light. The dried specimens resemble small seeds. Because of their retention of the power to luminesce, *Cypridina* have been widely used as experimental animals in living-light studies and most of this research has been carried out in Japan. It is interesting to consider the fact that bioluminescence, whether of the firefly or *Cypridina*, is basically the same; it involves similar chemical reactions.

The eyes of humans are not well adapted to night vision; it has been our habit for endless generations to curtail our activities after nightfall. On the other hand, many wild creatures have special adaptations enabling them to see better in dim light. We say that a cat can see in the dark, but this is actually not so; a cat's eyes are so constructed that they can see much better in dim light than we can. No animal can see in complete darkness. The eye is very much like a camera and a camera cannot take pictures in the total absence of light regardless of how sensitive the film with which it is loaded. The retina, or light-sensitive layer, of the eye has two types of sensory receptors, the *rods* and the *cones*. There are millions of these cells, all packed together like matches in a box. There are about 125 million rods and about 7 million cones in the human eye. The rods are especially sensitive to dim light while the cones are sensitive to bright light. There are more cones near the center of the retina, however, and this is the region of keenest vision in bright light. Thus, the outer portions of the retina contain, proportionately, more rods and are more sensitive to dim light. For this reason, under conditions of poor light, objects can be seen best if the eye does not look directly at them. During my years in the U. S. Navy, I was trained to scan the horizon during night watches not by looking directly at the horizon but some distance above it.

The eyes of nocturnal animals have large numbers of rods and few cones, while the eyes of diurnal animals have mostly cones. Most birds are active only by day and their eyes have many cones. By contrast, owls are nocturnal in habit and their eyes have many rods. The same is true of flying squirrels.

It is an interesting fact, too, that, as the light fades, colors disappear. Near the stump on which I am seated is a trumpet creeper with tubular blooms. Before the coming of dusk, the blooms were orange in color but they now appear black. On the other hand, a short distance toward my left is a group of attractive white spider lilies growing in a moist spot. I noticed that as the light slowly decreased their blooms became more visible, an adaptation to attract the night-flying insects that pollinate them. Colorful blooms attract bees, butterflies, and other diurnal insects while white blooms attract crepuscular or nocturnal kinds. Each color serves its purpose. In general, at night or in dim light, objects are seen mainly in outline and their colors and details are absent.

Often at night I have roamed the island woods, using a flashlight to find the way. Sometimes, I have had the good fortune to focus on the eyes of nocturnal mammals which glowed in the light. The

Delicate plume-moths flit through the night, often alighting on the vegetation and folding their plume-like hind wings beneath their forewings.

reason for this is that the eyes of most wild animals have a layer of light-reflecting crystals in the choroid layer which lies just back of the retina. This reflective layer, called the *tapetum lucidum*, catches light rays and reflects them back to the sensitive retina, thus increasing the eye's power to see in dim light. It also makes the eyes glow in the darkness like reflectorized highway signs. This layer of crystals is absent in our eyes and so they do not shine in the headlights of a car or in the beam of a spotlight. The eyes of some fish emit a greenish glow in a spotlight, caused by a silvery or greenish golden choroid layer called the *argentea*.

An interesting sidelight, and one that is evidence of the close affinity between ourselves and the other primates, is the fact that few of these animals have reflective layers and so their eyes do not "shine in the dark." Similar substances are found in the eyes of some other animals; for instance, I have often shone a flashlight into the

With the coming of dusk, orb-weaving spiders build their intricate webs among the trees for the capture of night-flying insects. By morning, the webs are in tatters and the spiders must construct new ones with the arrival of another island night.

eyes of alligators in the surrounding bayous. In the beam of a light, an alligator's eyes glow deep red like twin coals of fire.

Some animals have no night vision at all; domestic chickens have only day vision and this is the reason that they go to roost at the first sign of dusk. It has often been noticed that chickens may even go to roost during times of total eclipses of the sun. Like domestic chickens, most wild birds go to sleep at dusk. If a biologist who knew nothing at all of an animal's habits could examine its eyes, he could easily tell whether it was nocturnal or not.

Seated comfortably on the top deck of the houseboat, I often pause at the end of the day's activities to enjoy that period when night slowly descends over the island and the river. From my seat I can look down upon the island and watch various birds settling down for sleep. Over there beside that clump of palmettos I notice a mockingbird; it hops about uncertainly as if seeking something, then flutters up into a hornbeam tree where it quiets down among the Spanish moss. Unless disturbed, it will remain there until dawn. In the tall marsh grasses growing along the river's margin I hear the incessant twittering of blackbirds searching for perches; gradually their voices fade as, one by one, they locate suitable sites for the night. By the time the daylight has disappeared the diurnal birds all have found roosting locations. Once on their perches, they will not leave since their eyes are not well suited to vision in dim light. Their feet are admirably adapted to grasping limbs and twigs, even in sleep. Strong tendons, passing down their legs and beneath their toes, cause their feet to grasp twigs or grass stems more or less automatically when the legs are bent. Once settled down on a twig for the night, a perching bird's toes are locked around it in a remarkable adaptation for arboreal life.

At night, as I make my way cautiously through the dense vegetation of the island forest, I am sure that many eyes watch my passing. I do not always see them but I know that they are there. All around me, when I turn on my light, I see tiny glints of light among the leaves and on the ground. These are the glowing eyes of spiders. Some of them are green or bluish while others are fire-red, but all of them probably watch my every movement and I am aware that I am not alone on my nocturnal wanderings.

Some distance inland, there is a slight depression in the forest floor where marsh plants of various kinds flourish in abundance. By day, it is one of my favorite spots since it is the habitat of numerous dragonflies that cruise about like tiny airplanes, alighting now and then on taller plants to rest their cellophane-like wings. But tonight the dragonflies are gone, safely hidden, I suppose, among the vegetation. By contrast, the night has been transformed by an amphibian throng that shatters the silence of the island with sound. The noise rises in a crescendo that hurts my ears, then fades away, only to rise again. The loudest frog call appears to come from a point near my feet so I bend down in search of its maker. By the volume, I estimate that the frog must be at least as large as my fist, so I am astonished when I at last discover it to be a cricket frog *(Acris)*, smaller than my thumb and attractively marked on its back with green and yellow. As I watch, the tiny creature expands the thin, white vocal sac beneath its throat and its voice is so out of proportion to its size that I fail to see how such a small animal can make such a loud noise. I attempt to capture it in my hand but its slimy body slips through my fingers and escapes.

At dusk, cricket frogs hidden among the grasses expand their vocal sacs and emit loud, rasping calls.

Farther on, I hear another, even louder frog call, and decide to approach more cautiously in the hope of obtaining a photograph. What I am hearing, I know, is the call of a green *Hyla* but it is difficult to locate. Frog calls, like those of katydids, have a ventriloquial characteristic, making the animals most difficult to find. I decide to be clever and try "triangulation," which I have found successful in locating crickets and katydids. I move several paces to the right and listen, trying to determine the direction of the sound. Then I move to the left and do the same. As nearly as I can tell, the sound appears to emanate from a clump of marsh grass at the water's edge. Approaching cautiously, I at last spy the creature—a green *Hyla*, as I suspected—perched on the grass in full view. Why I had such difficulty in locating it, I have no idea. Apparently the green coloration of these frogs protects them well.

Hidden behind the beam of my flashlight, I approach very closely and am able to watch as it blows out the vocal sac beneath its throat. Once expanded, the sac vibrates with a strident call that jars hoarsely on my ears at this close range.

Frogs of many kinds make sounds in this fashion and the mechanism is quite interesting. These amphibian nocturnes are produced in a rather unusual manner, one that, in a general way, is analogous to the heehaw of the jackass. In both cases they are produced by air being forced back and forth through vocal cords. By contrast, our voices result from air passing outward through vocal cords, not both ways.

While watching the green *Hyla*, I inadvertently brush against the grass upon which it is resting with the result that the frog is alarmed and ceases its vocal efforts. It deflates its sac and sits quietly, apparently aware that there is some disturbance in the vicinity. What always amazes me is the fact that so few nocturnal creatures are alarmed by artificial lights. The slightest sound disturbs them but the beam of a flashlight leaves them unmoved. I can only conclude that artificial lights are so foreign to their instinctive behavior as to cause no reaction at all. Anyway, after a few minutes the *Hyla* puffs out its vocal sac again and the air is once more filled with vi-

Here and there in The Island's forest, green tree frogs sit among the vines and leaves. Their thin vocal sacs serve as resonance chambers that increase the range of their calls.

brations. In a way, a frog's sound-making mechanism may be compared to a bagpipe; both the lungs and the vocal sac merely serve as reservoirs for air which is used over and over as it passes back and forth through the vocal cords. In addition, the thin, membranous walls of the vocal sac serve as a resonance chamber, greatly amplifying the call. Actually, there are two vocal sacs but, externally, they appear as one globular bag in the case of the *Hylas*. In some other frogs, the vocal sacs seem to arise from the sides of the neck.

Since the *Hyla* appears to be undisturbed by my presence, I set up my camera and electronic flash and begin snapping pictures. The brilliant flashes, accompanied by small bursts of heat, seem to bother the frog, but only to the extent that it twitches its hind legs each time a photograph is taken. Having no further interest in the green *Hyla*, I touch it with my finger and am amazed at its quick reaction; its slender hind legs propel it away through the air and it disappears in the marsh grass.

There is an area of open water beyond the fringing grass and I pass the beam of my light over it to see what else is there, if anything. Near a moss-covered log along the far side of the pool I see a cooter turtle, half-submerged. My activity has caused it to lift its head in moderate alarm and its eyes stare unblinkingly into the light. I am not particularly interested in cooter turtles; they are too common in the area. But it crosses my mind as being strange that evolution has neglected to endow these shell-bearing reptiles with voices of any sort. I recall King Solomon's comment on spring when "The flowers appear on the earth; the time of the singing of birds is come and the voice of the turtle is heard in our land." King Solomon was, of course, referring to the turtle dove, not to the silent reptile.

One of the more unusual fish found in the surrounding waters is the drum. Most fish make no sounds at all but the drum is an exception; the swim bladder of this fish is divided into two parts connected to each other by a narrow passage. It is believed that the drumming sound is produced by air being forced from one part of the swim bladder to the other. Often, on still summer nights, the

Green tree frogs (Hyla) *also perch on cypress knees along the margins of* the cypress lake. Their pad-like toes help them to crawl over the smooth surfaces. Their tadpoles develop in hidden pools.

peculiar grunting or croaking sounds of these fish can be heard along the Pascagoula and I have known them to follow beneath my rowboat, constantly emitting their noises. Certainly, "talking" fish are a rarity in fresh water, but the drum belongs to a very talkative piscine family whose members are mostly marine. The most common of these is the croaker that, like its cousin the drum, uses its swim bladder as a resonating chamber for sound production both in or out of water.

In the bayou areas along the Gulf Coast, the drum is known as the *gaspergou*, a name that was originally *Casse-Burgo*, meaning "shell-cracker," dating from the early French settlers. They are excellent eating, often attaining a weight of sixty pounds and feeding upon fresh-water mussels which are crushed between their powerful grinding teeth, a fact that brings up a strange paradox. The drum feeds upon mussels, but it in turn serves as a host for the young parasitic stage of these same mussels. Upon the bodies of the drums, the young mussels or glochidia, live as parasites for a time, then leave the fish and settle down to the bottom of the river or the bayou and grow into mussels. Thus in a sense the drum helps to produce its own food. They are among the strangest of all the local fish. I have sometimes heard their drumming late at night as I lay in my bunk aboard the houseboat. It is creepy and vaguely mysterious, like so many of the other noises heard along the river after darkness has settled down over its gently moving surface. The sounds of the day are familiar and understood but the island night has a thousand indefinable tones and voices, some distinct, others perhaps imagined, but all blending together into the soft symphony of the nocturnal river.

Thus, the sights and sounds of the island night drift around me as I pause from the day's activities. Across the river against the dark shore, fireflies now and again blink their lights like sparks, adding further mystery to the scene. I raise my eyes above the river and the forest where other points of light, infinitely more remote, are set like jewels in the velvet darkness of the sky. Overhead hangs the planet Saturn with its strange rings, while to the west the constellation of Orion, the Hunter, drops slowly toward the horizon, its seven bright stars eternally set in their pattern which has often guided men in their wanderings. Earth and island may change, nations may come and go, and the river flowing southward like a great snake with its head in the Gulf and its tail upon the land may slowly alter its meandering course. Only the heavens remain forever the same, imparting a sense of stability to a world where continuous change is the rule. Still, The Island changes but slowly as compared to the continental land, so I am sure that whenever I return on periodic visits, I shall find it much as it has always been. When away from this fascinating place I feel, in retrospect, its dream-like quality; I hear again the soft whisperings of the night-shrouded river, the mournful call of the great horned owl and the half-somnolent night songs of the birds. I envision the waving sea of marsh grass and, above all, the great trees clothed with gray-green Spanish moss. I hear the cicadas drumming high in the hornbeams and smell the fragrance of swamp bay leaves crushed between my fingers. Drawn by the lodestar magnetism of The Island, I know that I must return again to thrill anew to the wide vistas of islands and marshland and sky.

Index

Page numbers in *italics* are those on which illustrations appear